DATE DUE	
JUL 2 8 2001	
3.75	

A LERMONTOV READER

MIKHAIL YUREVICH LERMONTOV (1814–1841)
(photograph courtesy Sovphoto)

A Lermontov Reader

EDITED, TRANSLATED, AND WITH AN INTRODUCTION

BY *GUY DANIELS*

The Macmillan Company, New York

Certain of the poems in this volume have ap-
peared (in slightly different form) in *Poems and
Translations*, by Guy Daniels (Inferno Press Edi-
tions, 1959); in the anthology, *Poetry Los Angeles I*
(Villiers, 1958); in various numbers of *The Literary
Review* and *The Colorado Review;* and in *Voices.*
Some of the material in the Introduction was first
published in *The Kenyon Review.*

TO   PAUL   AND   FRIEDA   BRADLOW

Acknowledgments

I should like to express my gratitude, for a host of things ranging from general encouragement to close textual consultation, to: René Wellek, Sterling Professor of Comparative Literature, Yale University; Professor V. A. Manuylov, of Leningrad University; Mr. Emile Capouya, formerly Senior Editor at the Macmillan Company; Eve Merriam; and Victor Dukoff, M.D., of New York City. Mr. John Cournos, the *doyen* of America's Russian translators, provided some helpful advice in the early stages. Finally, I must thank the Authors' League Fund for prompt and generous response to two emergency appeals.

G.D.

Contents

Biographical Note

Perhaps the best account of Lermontov's life in English is the biographical chapter in Mikhail Lermontov *by John Mersereau, Jr., published in Crosscurrents Series, Southern Illinois University Press, 1962. Some keen insights into the poet's personality are to be found in Janko Lavrin's* Lermontov, *Bowes and Bowes, 1959.*

Mikhail Yuryevich Lermontov was born in Moscow on October 2 (O.S.) 1814. His father, a retired army captain, was descended from a Scots mercenary, George Learmont, who settled in Russia in the 17th century. His mother died when he was not yet three, and he was reared by his wealthy, widowed grandmother, Mme. Arseneva, aided by various private tutors, etc.

He entered Moscow University at age sixteen. Two years later, he suddenly (for reasons not yet clear) left Moscow for St. Petersburg, where he enrolled in the Cavalry Cadets' School. He was commissioned an "ensign" in the Life Guard Hussars in 1834, and began, so it would appear, to lead a rather dissipated life.

In the winter of 1837, Pushkin was killed in a duel and the younger poet wrote (and circulated) his famous accusatory poem, "Death of a Poet," for which he was court-martialed and "exiled" to the combat zone in the Caucasus. The rest of his brief life was a whirlwind of activity: constant quarrels with the authorities, banishments, feats of bravery in battle, fleeting love affairs, and (miraculously) intensive literary work. In the summer of 1841, less than four years after Pushkin's death, his rightful successor met the same fate: he was killed in a duel—"to the accompaniment of thunder and lightning."

Introduction

The decade between the Congress of Vienna and the
December Revolution of 1825 (corresponding, with a
shift of one year, to the first decade of Lermontov's life)
was a period of high excitement in Russia. Just before
it opened, that sprawling empire's "two cultures" (in
the pre-Snovian sense: the native Russian peasantry and
the quasi-foreign élite) had joined hands for the first
time, under the threat of the French invasion. Its outset
was marked by the triumphal return of Tsar Alexander I
from Vienna, full of high hopes for his Holy Alliance
and lavish with promises of better things to come. Meantime, some of his most brilliant officers were on their way
home from Paris (where they had lingered after entering
the city as victors in 1815) full of hopes equally high,
but of a distinctly different kind. These philosopher-
colonels and poet-generals of gentle birth, endowed with
vigorous minds, passionate natures, and an abiding admiration for the French Jacobins and/or the late General
George Washington, were to become the "Decembrists":
the makers of Russia's first modern-day revolution.

There was a close symbiosis, in those days, between
poetry and politics; so that in literature things were
equally lively. Zhukovsky was importing large shipments

of German and English romantic poetry into Russia via his own very skilful "imitations." Krylov, having abandoned his career as playwright, had chosen to "turn and live with animals," and so became the greatest fabulist of modern times. Griboyedov was creating the first masterpiece of modern Russian drama, *Woe from Wit*. And one, Alexander Pushkin, when he was not occupied with ladies of easy virtue or drinking toasts to freedom in the company of his Decembrist friends, was busy founding modern Russian poetry.

Right in the middle of this period Sir John Bowring, one of those peripatetic English gentlemen with a flair for political and cultural curiosities abroad, visited St. Petersburg. He hobnobbed with Krylov and others, labored hard at Russian (with the help of German "ponies"), and upon his return to London published *Specimens of the Russian Poets* (1821) which, for all I know, marks the beginning of that exacting and ill-paid but important métier: the englishing of Russian poetry.

Sir John's versions, though vigorous and even at times "compelling" (a word he would have scorned to use) leave somewhat to be desired in the matter of accuracy. But this didn't discountenance him in the least. On the contrary, in a footnote to his translation of Derzhavin's famous "Ode to God," he remarks: "There is in the first verse a variation from the original, which does not accord with my views of the perfection of the Deity."

"Quaint," I suppose one might say of this outlook; but not altogether in the sense of 'outmoded.' Rather recently (1959) Mr. Stephen Spender published a translation of

Schiller's *Mary Stuart* in which (he said) he had altered Schiller's portrayal of both Mary Stuart and Elizabeth I because they didn't "accord with the views" of the English public. Of the two rationales for tampering with a text, I must say I prefer Sir John's: it, at any rate, bears the stamp of sturdy individualism.[1]

Further observations on the specifics of Russian-English translation will be found in *A Few Technicalities* (*see infra*). I put the above comments where they are because it was my intention to begin this Introduction with a few disclaimers as to what *A Lermontov Reader* is not. And one of the things it is not—quite unequivocally—is a compendium of "imitations," "adaptations," etc. Throughout this book, the "ideas" in general, the metaphors, even (in much of the poetry) the very rhythms, are Lermontov's, not mine. The English text is often, in fact, so close to the original that the former could serve as a "trot" or "crib." But even if so, such a consideration is secondary. Because this *Reader* was likewise not conceived (at the other extreme from "imitations") as a glorified Teaching Aid, but as literature. In short, if my versions from Lermontov's Russian poems do not stand up as *poems in English,* they are failures—"faithful" failures perhaps, but failures nonetheless.

Another thing this book is not, is "the definitive edition of all of the best works of Mikhail Lermontov (1814–41)."

---

[1] Lermontov, in a letter written when he was seventeen, objected violently to the plastic surgery done on *Hamlet* (which he knew in the original) by French and Russian "adaptors" to make it "accord with the views" of French and Russian theater audiences of 1831. He preferred Shakespeare's views, he said.

First, it is not a "definitive edition" for the simple reason that there is no such thing. Editions of a writer's works evolve—for better or for worse—like everything else on this planet. Thus there have been a great many editions of Lermontov's works in Russian (plus a goodly number in other languages); and there will no doubt be a great many more. (The hundreds of Lermontov specialists in the Soviet Union, unbemused by any notions of metaphysical "definitiveness," labor mightily to improve each successive edition; and they usually succeed.[2]

Nor is there any good reason why this first (and oh, so long overdue!) selection of Lermontov's poetry and prose should forever and always remain the *only* one available in our language. The time will come, I daresay, when there will be far more than a mere dozen or so English-speaking poets who know Russian. And when it does, we should expect to get—along with versions from such important and relatively "unexploited" *oeuvres* as those of Blok, Tyutchev, and Annensky—more of Lermontov. To be sure, we have long had a liberal sprinkling of his lyrics in the anthologies. But except for some of Miss Deutsch's later versions, most of these bear the tell-tale traces of a Swinburne scholar's sabbatical.

Second, this *Reader* does not contain "all of the best works of Mikhail Lermontov (1814–1841)." It does not contain *A Hero of Our Time,* Lermontov's best-known prose work, for two reasons: 1) because *Hero* is currently

[2] Such are the meager consolations available to *amateurs* of literature, be they Russian or other, in this Atomic-yet-Argentine Age when "a cloud of critics, of compilers, of commentators" has "darkened the face of learning"—Gibbon.

available in three paperback editions, and presumably
will remain available so long as paperbacks and neo-
nihilism are with us; i.e., for the entirety of the foresee-
able future; 2) because I felt it necessary to give over the
space in question to works hitherto unavailable in English (and most of the material in this *Reader* falls under
that head) in order to correct the badly distorted image,
so long entertained in the English-speaking world, of
Lermontov as a *homo unius libris.* Nor does it contain
"Sashka," that boisterous, bawdy, and beautiful poem
which, says Mirsky, is ". . . a genuine and lawful son of
Byron's *Don Juan*—perhaps the only one of all his progeny
who really looks like his father." There is a real need for
another English version of "Sashka." [3] But there is no
great need for it in the present selection, since Lermontov
as verse satirist is well represented by "The Tambov
Treasurer's Wife" and the excerpt from "A Fairy-Tale
for Children."

Finally, the other important omissions (i.e., of certain
short poems that have become classics in Russian) are
due to a fact that is, nine times out of ten, cravenly
ignored by translators and/or editors of volumes like the
present one. The usual practice, today, in most of the
non-English-speaking countries, is simply to disregard
problems of translation entirely (as in France or Russia).
Full speed ahead, and the devil take the hindermost, seems

[3] A translation of the poem by one John Pollen (who gave it the title
of "Moscow") was published in London in 1917 in an anthology called
Russian Songs and Lyrics (London, East and West, Ltd.). Of Lermontov's
three splendid satirical "tales in verse," "Sashka" is the only one to have
been englished until now. Quite a lacuna.

to be the *mot d'ordre*. This is quite unacceptable (and terribly provincial). The usual practice in the English-speaking world is to announce that "translation is, obviously, impossible," and then to go ahead and present a thick tome of translations. This is, obviously, schizophrenic. The analyzable facts are that *some* of a poet's works are totally refractory to, say, englishing (e.g., Mallarmé's swan sonnet, much of Rilke, etc.). Or it may even be that the entire tonality of a major work is inaccessible to the translator's own language, as Mr. Ciardi takes care to note in introducing his versions of Dante. But quite often, for every refractory poem in a poet's *oeuvre*, there is one that can be "brought back" more or less alive; and this applies particularly to Russian-English translating.

In the case of Lermontov, the satirical poems come across rather well—because they are largely "idea," and for other reasons noted elsewhere; but several of his best-known lyrics have a tonality (vowel coloration, and so on) that can only be travestied, not translated, in English.[4] Hence my omission, in this *Reader*, of such anthology pieces as "The Cossack Cradle Song," the two exquisite "Prayers," etc. Similarly, the famous "Borodino" was left out because the colloquialisms of the old veteran who describes that storied battle can properly be savored only in Russian.[5] (I should also mention, in the former cate-

---

[4] Conversely, it is quite impossible to put into Russian (or, God forbid, a romance language!) the potent English monosyllables of Donne—or of Thomas's

Split all ends up they shan't crack.

[5] Colloquialisms are always the translator's *bête noire;* and the problem is *not* solved by putting them into Cockney, Lalans, or whatever dialect that immediately transports the reader, in his imagination, to the British Isles, the Bronx, or the High Sierra.

gory, those aria-like passages in "The Demon" which are by now its sole saving grace.)

Finally, certain of the famous "poems of indictment" (e.g., "Death of a Poet") have been omitted because they are essentially displays of rhetoric—better than, but similar to, the declamation pieces of Yevtushenko.

On the other hand, lest I myself be accused of the opposite kind of craven behavior, I point with pride to the presence in this volume of a poem which, said Belinsky, "could not be translated into any other language." I refer to that rather short narrative poem with a title as long as that of a Soviet government agency: "A Song about Tsar Iván Vasíl'yevich, the Young Bodyguard, and the Valorous Merchant Kaláshnikov." "Kalashnikov" (today generally regarded as Lermontov's poetic masterpiece) is indeed a rough go for the translator: its heavy, rather Burgundian rhythms, its evocation of medieval Moscow in semi-archaic Russian, and so on, are perhaps, in the final analysis, "untranslatable," as Belinsky said. All I know for sure is that no one before me has ever struggled so long and so hard to fit the stress patterns of English into the bumpy Procustean (cornhusk?) mattress of the original.

Since this first section of the Introduction is dedicated to the proposition that the reader of a volume like the present one is entitled, first off, to an accounting of the sampling methods used, right here is probably the best place to eke out that accounting with data on the *size* of the sample. (For other "factual information" of the kind found in the reference books, *cf.* the foregoing Biographical Note.)

The Lermontov corpus consists, my IBM machine tells me, of over three hundred lyrics, some twenty-five narrative poems, five plays, three novels (two incomplete), one short story, and miscellaneous items including some very interesting but very "unliterary" letters in both Russian and French. (The machine further reports, with exemplary dispassion, that this output ceased abruptly with a "total failure of the production unit" at the age of 26 years, 9 months, and 12 days.) So that our selection represents: of the lyrics, about 5 percent; of the narrative poems, about 10 percent; of the plays, 20 percent; of the novels, 33⅓ percent; and of the rest, zero percent. Our sample, then, is a smallish one—but rightly so, because in this body of work there is a very great preponderance of juvenilia. As the youthful poet said in one of his verses about Byron,

> I started sooner, I'll end sooner . . .

And he did.

I I

"Pushkin erected the house of our spiritual life, the edifice of Russia's historical awareness. Lermontov was its first tenant." [6]
—PASTERNAK

Modern Russian poetry, which preceded and nourished that gusher of great prose works commonly taken to be identical with "Russian literature," was founded by a Russian Negro (I here employ the standard American criterion for such distinctions: he was an octoroon) named

---

[6] Letter to Eugene M. Kayden. Quoted in *Poems by Boris Pasternak*, translated by Eugene M. Kayden.

Alexander Sergeyevich Pushkin (1799–1837). There had been no great tradition of pre-modern Russian poetry to look back to (no Chaucer, Dante, Shakespeare, or Racine) so that he had to start largely from scratch. There was, however, an abundance of folk poems to draw upon; and he did get a few assists from Lomonosov (1711–65) and Derzhavin (1743–1816) in the matter of majesty, Zhukovsky (1783–1852) in the matter of melody, and Krylov (1769–1844) in the matter of putting colloquial expressions into fluid, elegant lines of poetry.

Building on the language reforms of Nicholas Karamzin (1766–1826) and the technical innovations of Zhukovsky, Pushkin forged, welded, molded, and generally put together the language of modern Russian poetry.[7] He mixed the lofty with the lowly, the sweet with the sour, created modulations never heard before (in Russian or any other language), and introduced a kind of Flemish realism—homely detail suffused with the golden limpidity of his line—therein breaking away from that French eighteenth century tradition (both poetic and intellectual) to which in most other respects he remained committed. His poetic practice, in other words, ran ahead of his thinking—which was to be expected in one who was first and foremost an artist.

Pushkin and his pleiad (Baratynsky, Yazykov, *et al.*) enjoyed great popularity during the first half of what has come to be known as the Golden Age of Russian litera-

[7] The only major contribution to this work made after Pushkin was Lermontov's: in particular, he extended the range of rhyme, used a much more varied metrics, lessened the rigidity of line-units.

ture: a mere decade (1820–30) split right down the middle by the December Revolution. It was an age of poetry; and a novel written in verse, Pushkin's *Eugene Onegin,* was perhaps its finest fruit—the first major Russian work in that genre. But its exuberance—and hence its poetry—was badly damped down by the December Revolution and its grim aftermath; and it remained only for the novels of Sir Walter Scott to deliver the coup de grâce.

The turning away toward prose begins in 1829–30, when Scott's novels first began to appear in Russia. Later in the 'Thirties, several of Pushkin's finest poems appeared; and he also published, in his magazine *The Contemporary,* generous selections from a poet who was perhaps a greater lyricist than himself: Fyodor Tyutchev (1803–73). But nobody paid any attention: prose (and especially Sir Walter Scott) was all the rage. Pushkin, though, was a professional if there ever was one; and as early as 1830, he himself had "embraced" the medium of prose.

That embrace, however, lacked some of the fervor he had felt for the Muse. His prose writings are all admirable in their way. They are "neat," they create atmospheres of whatever variety with great skill, and they contain some excellent character-drawing; e.g., the two feuding country squires in "Dubrovsky," and the old captain in "The Captain's Daughter." [8] But poetry was to Pushkin as water to the fish: out on dry land he had (quite liter-

---

[8] This old captain is obviously a forerunner of Lermontov's Maxim Maximych in *Hero.* Prof. N. L. Stepanov of Moscow University, in one of his books on Krylov, says that Pushkin's life model was Krylov's father, about whom the latter used to tell his young friend numerous anecdotes from the days of the Pugachev Rebellion.

ally) difficulty breathing, with the curious result that his prose is sometimes contrived, where his poetry never is.

For a time, Russian prose was stagnant and imitative, by and large. Then a young Ukrainian who had failed as a poet, began to publish collections of his short stories and, in 1836, a play called *The Inspector-General.* With the arrival of Nikolay Gogol (1809–52) on the scene, and his infusion of new life into Russian prose, the eclipse of poetry seemed more total than even before.

Such, in broad outline, was the state of Russian letters when, in January 1837, Pushkin was killed in a duel and Lermontov, as a consequence of dashing off his inflammatory "Death of a Poet," achieved a notoriety followed soon thereafter by the draping of the Master's mantle over the resplendent dress uniform of a lieutenant in the Life Guard Hussars.

III

> *Why did he shake hands with worthless slanderers?*
> *Why did he trust false words and flattery?*
> —"Death of a Poet"

About four-fifths of classic Russian literature gets its primary motive power from forceful female characters. The men talk eloquently about their ideals (or lack of ideals); but they do not so much act as allow themselves to be acted on by the women. Herewith a few specimens from the Russian literature upon which Lermontov was weaned.

The best Russian comedy of the eighteenth century, Fonvizin's *Hobbledehoy* or *The Minor* (first performed

1782) is entirely animated by the crude, greedy, and stupid but very "dynamic" willfulness of Mme Prostkova ("Mme Simpleton").

Chatsky, the hero of Griboyedov's *Woe from Wit* (written 1822–24), is by exception a fairly strong male character (though more of a "talker" than a "doer"). Nonetheless, the play ends with his getting out of town after his childhood sweetheart, Sofiya, who has already denounced him for "maligning Moscow," [9] helps start a rumor that he is insane. And in the curtain line Sofiya's father, Famusov, asks himself in fear and trembling: "What will Princess Marya Aleksevna say?" [10]

The main line of development in Pushkin's *Eugene Onegin* (written 1823–31) has its source in the weakness of Eugene and the strength of Tatyana. To be sure, Tatyana is admirable as far as the story takes us " . . . and they lived unhappily ever after"); and she has inspired countless portraits of admirable, "firm" female characters since. But let it not be forgotten that her mother—herself a "dreamer" in her girlhood—came in later years to relish the role of despot in her little domain.

The three works ensampled above are the most important landmarks in Russian literature for the half-

[9] In a recent American translation of the play, this famous line, used by Pushkin as an epigraph for Chapter VII of *Eugene Onegin*, comes out: "Driving into Moscow!" (!)

[10] A bit of cruel historical irony. In 1828, Griboyedov represented the Russian Government in negotiating a peace treaty with Persia. In 1829, then Minister to Persia, he was hacked to pieces by a mob which stormed the Russian Legation in Teheran. The Persian protest was provoked mainly by a provision of the treaty requiring them to surrender up the Christian women they had taken into their harems—where, one supposes, they were *not* behaving willfully.

century in question. From this point on, the list could be extended through the Great Prose Realists [11] right up to *Doctor Zhivago*. And for good measure, we might toss in those Soviet recruiting posters of World War II bearing the image of a youngish Russian Mother whose facial expression compounds Love and Stern Admonition in a ratio of 3.751 to 6.249. (Does she have a name, I wonder?)

The Female Principle has been the object of a few minor rebellions, of course. Pushkin (a major poet but a minor rebel) even waged, in his careless youth, a lighthearted (and half-hearted) campaign against the Divine Prototype. In his mock epic, *The Gavriliad* (1821) he has the Virgin Mary seduced three times in one day: by Gabriel, by the Devil first appearing as a serpent, and by the Holy Ghost appearing as a dove.[12]

Lermontov was notorious for his blasphemy and satanism. (After he was killed, the house in which he had been living was sprinkled with holy water.) And he was as crude as Pushkin in his dealings with prostitutes and serf girls. But it is inconceivable that he should ever have vilified Mary.[13] He was the Great Rebel of Russian literature (the only one, said Merezhkovsky, who never gave in); and the major rebels, as we know, never choose a lesser opponent than the Creator against whom to meas-

---

[11] With some obvious exceptions, especially in the works of Tolstoy. But then Turgenev more than makes up for them.

[12] In perhaps the highest dramatic moment in *Boris Godunov* (written four years later) when Boris requests the saintly idiot to pray for him, the latter refuses, saying, "The Mother of God won't allow it."

[13] The two lovely "Prayers" mentioned earlier are both addressed (one of them only implicitly, to be sure) to Mary. Both are grudgingly admired by the Soviet critics, who consider them as instances of "backsliding." (I am not prepared to dispute this statement.)

ure themselves. Most of Lermontov's life from his early
teens onward was such a struggle—a contest "between
men"; and the blow-by-blow account we get of it in his
works is delivered in a preëminently masculine voice.

It was precisely the *masculine strength* of that voice
that so "astounded the world" when it was first heard [14]
in that bleak winter of 1837; and it is to these same qualities that Lermontov owes his place of high eminence in
Russian literature—an eminence sometimes regarded
askance by non-Russians (as, indeed, by Russians who know
only his anthology pieces). What Belinsky admired most
of all in him—and Belinsky did more than anyone else
to found Lermontov's reputation—was his "great power."
Turgenev, who saw him in 1840, noted in his journal that
Lermontov possessed "a strength immediately recognized
by everyone." Gogol, who knew him, was one of those
who recognized that strength, together with its treacherous
nature—which made him fear for the poet. Mirsky declared that, had Lermontov not died so young, "he
might have shown the Russian novel a manlier and
stronger way than it actually took." Tolstoy, as we know,
had only contempt for most poetry and poets; but he
remained firm in his admiration for those "three equally
great poets: Pushkin, Lermontov, and Tyutchev." And
of the youngest he said: "He started right in, like a man
of real power."

The trouble is that there are so many kinds of strength;
and the trouble with most Lermontov criticism is that

[14] One youthful poem had been published some years before without
Lermontov's consent, and had passed unnoticed.

it does not distinguish one kind of strength from another. The paranoid will-to-power displayed by Pechorin in *A Hero of Our Time*, for instance, is all too often taken as a manifestation of his (and Lermontov's) "strength." It is quite to be expected that power on this level will be admired (along with mere, sheer physical strength—which as it happens, both the poet and his fictional character possessed) by vulgar readers in general; and that it be especially admired, in our own day, by quasi-literate punks fond of flaunting their "nihilism." [15] But it comes as something of a shock to find these two manifestations of "strength"—the one simply vulgar, the other morbid— recommended by that most unvulgar Cantabridgian gentleman and latter-day Russian Formalist, Vl. Nabokov. I have in mind his Foreword to the translation of *Hero* done by himself and Dmitri Nabokov, from which Pechorin emerges as a kind of cynical Steve Canyon whose "lasting appeal . . . , especially to young readers" is due *inter alia* to his "tigerlike suppleness and eagle eye, . . . elegance and brutality, delicacy of perception and harsh passion to dominate, ruthlessness and awareness of it, . . . ," etc., etc.

The "strength" admired in Lermontov by his friends and the best of his contemporaries—and by Kropotkin, Mirsky, and others since—was something quite different. In Tolstoy's terribly old-fashioned and "square" language it was that ". . . unending, powerful seeking for truth" that made him the equal of Pushkin. For Tolstoy, Ler-

---

[15] Lermontov himself would have called it their "nothingness" (*nichto-zhestvo*).

montov was a poet who "concealed, beneath his inflated Byronism, the highest moral requirements." So Belinsky, so Herzen, so Gogol—thinking of the poet in those moments when he was not, in Gogol's words, "toying so frivolously with his talent." Heartened by Tolstoy's example, I venture now to be terribly square myself and declare that the famous Author's Introduction to *Hero*, which Nabokov counsels us to ignore as "a stylized bit of make-believe," is to be taken quite seriously: quite as seriously as, for instance, the bit of "psychoanalysis" we get from the "Third Guest" at the end of *A Strange One*. In other words, that *Hero* is just what Lermontov says it is: the case history—or rather, a record of the terminal stages—of a disease. And I might add that only a person who did not know all of Lermontov's work really well could think it was anything else.[16]

The classic description of this phenomenon is of course the one given by Camus in *L'Homme révolté* (in the course of which, incidentally, he twice quotes Lermontov). The revolt of the "dandy," he tells us, begins with an excess of unemployable love, develops from this to the fury of "outraged innocence," and ends in satanism or "demonism": a compulsion to do evil "out of nostalgia for an unattainable good" (*"par nostalgie d'un bien impossible"*). This entire description fits Lermontov's case exactly (as it does that of de Vigny and others, of course) with only one exception: the Last Phase—wherein, says

---

[16] The question as to the etiology of this disease ("social causation vs. "intrapsychic factors," etc.) can be argued *ad infinitum*—and almost has been. But few critics in their right minds *deny its existence.*

Camus, if the "dandies" haven't committed suicide or gone mad, they "make a career for themselves and pose for posterity." [17] This is latter-day dandyism: Lermontov would never, never have become a careerist like Petrus Borel.

This is a good account. But an even better one can be found, *telescoped into one scene* (Scene VII), in *A Strange One*. In this one scene our sixteen-year-old poet achieved a kind of "dramatic miniaturization" comparable, perhaps, only to what was being done by his greater (as a dramatist) German contemporary, Georg Büchner: he capsulized the entire pattern of his own lifelong rebellion. (This alone is enough to make *A Strange One*, for all its mawkishness and inflated rhetoric, an important piece of literature. Yet the same scene gives us, besides, unmatchable lines like: "You gave me life—take it back!" And we get other *éclairs en profondeur*—into "the lower depths," one is tempted to say—of "the family romance" not unlike the nightmarish truths glimpsed, in our own day, through the prismatic poetry of Gil Orlovitz.)

All this is a far cry from Pushkin—that obviously virile but somehow less *"mâle"* man of letters [18] whose "wholeness" is so often contrasted with Lermontov's "split personality" and profound alienation. It is of course the difference (with a difference, however) between the eighteenth century and the nineteenth. Pushkin is a late-blooming flower of the French eighteenth century—

[17] In the American edition, this comes out: ". . . and pursue prosperity." (!) Such, I suppose, must needs be the psychopathology of everyday life under State Capitalism.

[18] "Neither Lermontov nor I was ever a man of letters"—Tolstoy.

with a strong dash of Russian (and Flemish) matter-of-factness, plus African sensuality, added to make him uniquely great. Lermontov is nineteenth century romanticism at its most intense; yet he was the first Russian writer to cast the cold eye of "serious prose realism" (in Auerbach's sense) upon the society around him: not in *Hero,* but in the earlier novel, *Princess Ligovskaya.*

The late Soviet critic, Boris Eichenbaum (Eykhenbaum) once had occasion to point out that whereas the Onega River flows smoothly down to the sea, the Pechora is twisting and tumultuous. In other words, however much Lermontov learned from Pushkin, in the most important respects he was his master's antithesis.[19] (Lermontov always got A's in geography.) Pushkin was balanced, "whole," and essentially moderate except in his more violent amours. Lermontov oscillated between despair and gaiety (like Heine, like Musset); and with a true romantic's "thirst for the infinite," he plunged headlong into everything: literature, music, mathematics, painting, reckless feats of horsemanship, other strenuous sports (including of course amatory jousting), daredevil performances in combat and, finally, the dueling that was to be the end of him. Pushkin wrote his "odes to freedom" while young, but became much more "reasonable" in later years—though now and then a spark flared up. Lermontov had his moments of chauvinism (though not so regrettable as Pushkin's) and never could quite decide whether he was for or against the "wild, free" tribesmen

19 I am at this point extending the analogy beyond what Professor Eichenbaum intended, i.e., the evident contrasts between Onegin and Pechorin.

of the Caucasus he slashed with his saber (while they were trying to slash him). But he never for a minute had any doubts about his opinion of Nicholas I and the people around him. (Nicholas, needless to say, reciprocated these feelings.) [20] And, finally, Pushkin didn't ever really have much of a struggle with his own demon (and a very "petty demon" it was, as even his foremost admirer, Belinsky, had to admit); whereas Lermontov fought all his life against his own "dark forces"—a losing battle, as it turned out.

They read the same literature, but with different eyes—and hearts: in Russian, the poets mentioned above, plus the splendid prose satirists of the eighteenth century (Novikov, Fonvizin, Krylov) and, above all, the works of Alexander Radishchev, which were forbidden by the authorities.[21] They both read French literature (almost all of it, so one gathers); and they read the German and English romantics, including that proto-romantic, Wm. Shakespeare—Pushkin using French translations (until his later years), Lermontov *penché sur les textes* of the originals, starting in his middle teens. (His "imitations" of Goethe, Schiller, Heine, Byron, Moore, *et al.* are superb: better than the originals in many cases.)

More than anything else, it was the romantics that they

[20] Whether or not Major Martynov, whose pistol shot killed Lermontov, was an "agent" of the Tsar, there is absolutely no doubt that Nicholas I was "out to get" the poet. But then it was no problem: Lermontov obviously wanted to die anyway.

[21] Radishchev (1749–1802), nobleman, "college classmate" of Goethe at Leipzig, etc., was the great granddaddy of all modern-day Russian revolutions. *See* his *Journey from St. Petersburg to Moscow*—the book for whose publication he was sent to Siberia (after nearly having been executed).

read with different eyes and hearts. For Pushkin, the man of the eighteenth century, the romantic attitudes were little more than a literary stance—an interesting technical device. He read a lot of Byron (in French) for example; but he acquired hardly more than a smattering of the English poet's proud defiance. What he took from Byron was technical: his *manner* of telling a tale in verse: the development, the lyrical asides, the exoticism. And when he did reach real depth levels in his "Byronic" tales, it was only to discredit the romantic "pose," as in *The Gypsies*; or to spoof it, while yet half-indulging in it, as in *Eugene Onegin*.[22]

His attitude, very professional, is precisely what we see today in Vl. Nabokov, who assures us that Pechorin is ". . . the fictional descendant of a number of fictional self-analysts . . . ," after which he goes on to name Pechorin's obvious antecedents: St. Preux, Werther, René, Adolphe, Byron's heroes, and Onegin himself. This is a truism on the high-school textbook level, and altogether unexceptionable of course. What one does object to, however, is the following *ergo*: that, *since* Pechorin had a literary lineage (like Hamlet, like Humbert Humbert) he *therefore* didn't represent the particular *mal* of his own *siècle*. And anyway, it's all "stylized make-believe."

Pushkin, as I said, made the same kind of mistake.

[22] *Onegin* is in a sense a double spoof on both Byronic (Onegin) and Schilleresque (Lensky) romanticism: yet Pushkin indulged himself in both while spoofing them. Surely there is no more lushly romantic aria than that sung by Lensky in Act II of Tchaikovsky's opera based on *Onegin*; and the music fits exactly the words taken almost verbatim from Pushkin's text (Lensky's letter to Olga the night before his duel with Onegin). But how many music lovers know that, in the next lines, Pushkin says: "He let his weary head droop down/Over the fashionable word *ideal*/And quietly dozed off."

Quite explicitly, in the last chapter of *Onegin,* he advises his own hero to "abandon this outmoded fashion" (of Byronic alienation) because he has "already pulled the leg of society often enough." And back in 1792 Krylov, another fine artist ahead of his own time in the creation of *forms* but not always abreast of its historical development, did the same thing. In one of those bold and brilliant satirical sketches he wrote in his youth, at the very end of Catherine the Great's short-lived encouragement of satire, he japed Rousseau's notion that men of intelligence were "everywhere persecuted" by society.[23] The story was published early in 1792. In May 1792, the police raided the printing press of "Krylov and Associates." That man of intelligence, Ivan Krylov, was compelled to leave St. Petersburg; and his career as a prose satirist came to an abrupt end.

The point is that whereas some of the purely "formal" aspects of romantic alienation may have been "outmoded" by 1830 (when the last chapter of *Onegin* was written) [24] the *basic attitude itself* was more indispensable than ever. But Pushkin was to much the professional literary man to see this. For him, romantic revolt was *primarily a matter of literary convention*: Onegin was "a fictional descendant" of numerous fictional ancestors, *et voilà tout.* (After all, he had pretty much quelled his own mild rebellion; why shouldn't he quell, by means of gentle ridicule, that of his hero?) And so Russia's most incredibly gifted

---

[23] In the main, however, this story ("A Panegyric on My Late Grandfather"), a caricature of a Russian country squire, was very timely—too much so, no doubt. Its echoes can be clearly heard in the "false panegyrics" of Gogol a half-century later.

[24] I.e., Chapter VIII—not the later "Onegin's Travels."

poet, who had been a bit of a firebrand in his youth, demonstrated his "wholeness" in his maturity by seeking an accommodation with "temporal power."

It was an eminently "reasonable" choice—but a choice that made the last years of his life among the most miserable in the annals of literature. He began his "accommodation" by writing several poems of a temporizing nature (they are among his poorest works) in one of which he actually compared Nicholas I to Peter the Great! [25] By the time the middle of this "era of good feeling" was reached he was writing first lines like

Please God, let me not go mad!

And the whole thing ended—after he had undergone countless humiliations at court, including obligatory appearances there in the hated uniform of a "Gentleman of the Chamber," constant police surveillance, the opening of his letters to his wife by the censors, etc.—in his death in a duel: a death that cannot even be called tragic because so essentially stupid. (Like his own character, Lensky, whom he had sympathetically chided for his naïveté in defending the honor of his insipidly pretty but frivolous and flirtatious fiancée, Pushkin was killed defending the honor of his beautiful but equally frivolous and flirtatious wife.)

Such was the "absurd" fate of that Mozartean spirit of light, that Ariel of the frozen North, who had "matured" into a *pater familias* (four children) and a "whole man."

[25] The Soviet critics are no doubt correct in explaining this shameful poem as a bid for clemency on the part of Nicholas toward Pushkin's Decembrist friends in Siberia. But his bid was foredoomed to failure—*as he should have known.*

Meantime in the year 1830, when Pushkin was writing off Onegin's Byronic alienation, a fifteen-year-old poet of already deeply "divided" personality—but with a much more profound understanding of society and the historical process—was getting into a fine rage over the Master's apostasy and attempts at "accommodation." Because Lermontov understood, as Pushkin never did, that romantic alienation was *not merely a matter of literary modes*; that while certain purely formal aspects of the romantic revolt had perhaps become "old hat" to those concerned with literary novelties, the basic attitude of defiance toward "temporal power" was more indispensable than ever to a free spirit—and most especially to a free spirit who had had "the great misfortune" (as Pushkin himself had once put it) to be born into this particular time and place.

Quite naturally, what infuriated the teen-age poet more than anything else, was the Master's prostitution of poetry in this whole process of accommodation: the poem about Peter the Great and Nicholas I, for example, was just too much. And so, in the year 1830, at age fifteen, Lermontov sat down and wrote a strong reprimand—a *rappel à l'ordre* —to his idol, beginning

Oh, stop making excuses for depravity!

And he went on to admonish the Master to quit trying to please "those bastards" [26] and get back to his job of defending freedom.

But of course nobody ever saw the poem (Pushkin,

[26] The dictionary equivalents for the Russian—outmoded, as usual—are: "miscreant," "rascal," "scoundrel," etc. But in today's American we say "bastards."

had he seen it, would perhaps have been amused, but nothing more); and of course the great poet in the uniform of a "Gentleman of the Chamber" (a function usually reserved for much younger men) went on trying to "do business" with Nicholas and his court; and of course the whole thing ended as we have said.

And so once again, in that hideous winter of 1837, the younger poet—by now a lieutenant in the Life Guard Hussars—was compelled by the Master's moral myopia to take pen in hand. Once again the "whole man's" policy of "accommodation" had failed; and he of the "divided personality," the alienated soul, had to set things straight. But this time there was no recalling Pushkin to order: he was beyond the hail even of Lermontov's powerful voice.

So the younger poet began by putting questions to himself:

Why did he shake hands with worthless slanderers?

And out of his tortured self-interrogation and the wrath, then, that rose higher and higher, came the totally fearless "J'Accuse!" known as "Death of a Poet."

IV

> . . . *This delirium*
> *Obsessed my mind for many years. And then,*
> *Having disowned my other dreams as worthless,*
> *I rid myself of it by means of verses.*
> —"A Fairy-Tale for Children" (1840)

The important thing about Lermontov (said Belinsky in his magnum opus, *The Works of Alexander Push-*

kin) [27] is not whether he was the equal of Pushkin, or even greater: what counts is that he had greater problems to solve.

Those "greater problems" arose from Lermontov's greater awareness of two kinds of reality: the social reality around him, and the even more threatening reality (as he makes very plain in *A Strange One*) of the dark forces within himself.

Both kinds of awareness are evident even in his most youthful work. Among the poems written in his mid-teens, for example, are such anthology pieces as "The Angel" (whose theme is the dichotomy of the sacred and the profane), "The Sail" (which epitomizes inner conflict with a precision and memorableness seldom equaled by any other poet), and "A Prophecy" (comparable, in both "social awareness" *and* perfection of execution, to Milton's sonnet on the Piedmont Massacre: no small feat for a teen-age poet). And his first three plays (*The Spaniards, Men and Passions*,[28] and *A Strange One*), all written in his mid-teens, combine passionate "social protest" with dramatization of that metaphysical revolt which, as we have said, is at bottom the subject of all his works. In *The Spaniards*, set in the Spain of the Inquisition, *all* of the good people are Jews, and *all* of the bad people are Christians: and this situation, believe it or not, is set forth very convincingly by our fifteen-year-old Christian poet in the year 1830. Yet its main theme is the struggle between Fernando (the hero: a foundling of Jewish origin)

27 Belinsky had announced his intention to make a similarly extensive critical study of both Lermontov and Gogol; but he died (at 37) before they could be begun.

28 The original title is in German: *Menschen und Leidenschaften.*

and his "Fate" (or his Creator). Likewise for *Men and Passions* and *A Strange One*, wherein the Spanish Jews are replaced by Russian serfs—with, however, the important difference that not *all* of the serfs are "good." (In the former play, for example, one of the key characters, a serf woman, is portrayed as completely corrupted by the money-worship of her owner.)

The other juvenilia consist of the unfinished novel about the Pugachev Rebellion, *Vadim*; a mass of lyrics which, for all their technical imperfections and "romantic abstractness," stand in strong contrast, for sheer passionate conviction, to Pushkin's perfect but altogether cold schoolboy poems; and a large swatch of Byronic verse tales of adventure about which the less said, the better.[29] Also, if we accept the customary division of Lermontov's *oeuvre* into youthful (1828–36) and mature (1837–41), the first category will have to include the two later plays, *Two Brothers* (1835–36) and *Masquerade* (1836), together with the novel *Princess Ligovskaya* (1836), to which we shall return shortly. As for the two later plays, the former is Lermontov's poorest effort in a genre which was perhaps his weakest; and the latter, though much admired by the Soviet critics and several times produced (and filmed) is badly flawed: by Lermontov's constant revisions in his frustrated attempts to get it past the "moral" objections of the censors; and by the obtrusive echoes of both Griboyedov and Shakespeare (*Othello*).

His mature period begins with two poems that were

[29] Lermontov himself was under no illusions about his youthful works: he included none of them in making the selections for his *Poems* (1840).

immediately hailed by almost everyone, from Belinsky to Nicholas I: [30] "Borodino" and "Kalashnikov," the former published in 1837, shortly after Lermontov's first "exile," and the latter in 1838. Both remain classics today; and "Kalashnikov" has come to be regarded as the finest "modern epic" in Russian. ("Modern epic" because it made use, for the first time in Russian classic poetry, of the rhythms and motifs of the *byliny* or folk epics.) Among other great virtues, "Kalashnikov" provides eloquent testimony in disproof of the frequent charge that Lermontov, like Byron, could write "only about himself." Its hero is a merchant, married, with two children. He is, in short, a "square"—a very rare phenomenon among romantic heroes.

The other long poems of the mature period fall into two categories: the romantic tales in verse ("The Demon," "Mtsyri") and the "ironic poems" ("Sashka," "The Tambov Treasurer's Wife," and "A Fairy-Tale for Children"). The latter are among the finest fruits of that state of mind known as "romantic irony": at least the equal of the best such work produced in Western Europe by Musset, Heine, *et al.* As for the former, "The Demon" was long regarded as Lermontov's poetic masterpiece, and is still so described in some of the handbooks. A more accurate description of it is that given by the poet's cousin, quondam roommate, and biographer, Shan-Girey, who said it was "a bad opera with some beautiful arias." "Mtsyri" ("The Novice" or "The Postulant") is more commonly regarded, today,

---

[30] Both poems were published unsigned, since Lermontov was still under a cloud following the scandal of "Death of a Poet."

as Lermontov's best poem in the romantic-rhetorical vein.

The short poems of the later period, comprising a good dozen or more that are among the best in Russian, can be grouped as lyrics of introspection ("I Walk Alone along the Highway"), "realistic lyrics" ("Native Land," "A Soldier's Testament") in which Lermontov develops the lead taken by Pushkin in this vein, "poems of indictment" ("Farewell, Unwashed Russia!"), and such unclassifiable items as the two "Prayers" aforementioned. The younger poet's continuing polemic with his late Master is most evident in the "poems of indictment." Thus his "Prophet" is a direct denial of Pushkin's exalted notions of the role of the poet, expressed in his own poem of the same title.

It has long been a critical commonplace that during this "mature" period, Lermontov was moving steadily away from his youthful romanticism and "demonism" toward "realism." That he did, indeed, produce later works that were highly "realistic" is quite evident. But, as Professor Manuylov has noted, this trend developed in parallel with—and not in opposition to—his romanticism. And nowhere is he more romantic than in that so-called "realistic" novel, *A Hero of Our Time.*

Hero can only be called realistic in the sense that Pechorin holds candid converse with himself in a manner quite unprecedented in the Russian novels of that day. But he himself is not at all "completely lifelike," as an American Slavic specialist recently called him. He is in fact "the Demon masquerading in an officer's uniform" (as some Russian writer, I forget which one, said long ago). This is evident above all in his omnipotence—his

"Superman" traits. Everybody and everything yields to him without the slightest struggle.[31] Especially the girls, of course; but also each and every one of his male rivals. So that we all know in advance, when he and Grushnitsky finally face each other, pistol in hand, who it is that will die.

On one plane, of course, this is merely harmless indulgence of very commonplace fantasies. But given the powerful drive of Lermontov's compulsion "to do evil out of a nostalgia for an unattainable good," it was not, perhaps, quite so harmless as all that. And in any case, it certainly was not "realistic" novel-writing.

He had come much closer to that a few years earlier, in *Princess Ligovskaya.* For all its purple patches and its clumsiness, *Ligovskaya* has much more of "serious prose realism" in it than does *Hero.* Its close scrutiny of social forces, shading of characterization, etc., make it altogether an astounding performance for a youth of twenty-one who was surely the most intensely passionate of all those intensely passionate poets known as the romantics.

Ligovskaya was also, on the personal plane, a strong start toward the kind of realism (in the sense of accepting life's necessary limitations) that might have saved Lermontov. And he had made a similar start, using "romantic irony" in poetic "self-analysis" of a thoroughly delightful kind, with "A Fairy-Tale for Children." Gogol, whose favorite poem among Lermontov's works was "Fairy-Tale," once declared that if the poet could have finished it, he

[31] The only one of the five stories (that make up the cycle of *Hero*) in which he is not omnipotent, is *Taman*—the first published, as I recall.

might have rid himself for good of that demonism that was threatening his very sanity.

But for reasons we shall never know, Lermontov finished neither the novel nor the poem. Instead, he completed *Hero*, which was published in 1840, the same year as his *Poems*. And in the summer of 1841, once again "exiled" to the combat zone in the Caucasus (for dueling with a French officer) he stopped off at the mountain resort of Pyatigorsk, as his fictional Pechorin had done. There he met up with one Major Martynov, who was much the same kind of "military fop" as Grushnitsky in *Hero of Our Time*. And, like Pechorin, Lermontov so humiliated his fellow officer that a duel was inevitable. Not being omnipotent, however, Pechorin's creator was killed with the first shot.

New York City
March 1964

A Few Technicalities

Patronymics ("Alexander *Son-of-Sergey* Pushkin") have for the most part been retained in this book. Certain revisionists in the translation of Russian literature, dead set on reducing the whole thing to the consistency of pablum, are possessed by a kind of theological hatred for that innocuous syllable *"ich"* (Alexander Sergeye*vich*) and are striving most zealously to exterminate it. These comrades are profoundly mistaken. The use of the patronymic to indicate a certain nuance in "interpersonal relationships" is very important in Russian *mores*—just as important as the American practice of nicknaming a casual acquaintance.

Consider, for instance, an American short story in which a politician backslaps a casual acquaintance, calling him "Bill," and then two days later stabs him in the same back he has recently slapped. This whole procedure—and especially the nicknaming—is an integral part of our *mores*.

Now consider a French translator of that same story who, following the usage *of his own country*, has the politician call his future victim "Monsieur." The whole point of the story is lost, is it not? The good translator (as George Moore long ago pointed out) takes care to preserve certain significant foreign tags (names of coins, etc.) in his work. These seeming trifles serve the very important purpose of reminding the reader that the story is not taking place in Sioux City, Iowa, in 1964, but in

Tambov in 1836 (or wherever and whenever). Patronymics serve just such a purpose—and others besides. So I have kept them.

I have also kept the *feminine forms of Russian last names* (e.g., Ligovskaya instead of Ligovskoy)—something else the revisionists feel duty-bound to eradicate. I have done this for the above mentioned reasons, plus one other. In a recent American translation of a famous Russian play, one of the scenes leaves the reader completely bewildered—until he finally discovers that the walk-on called "Karenin" (I have changed the name) is actually "Karenina." In other words, "Jones" turned out to be a woman! (This kind of thing used to happen to us in the Navy—sometimes with pleasant consequences, to be sure; but I thought we had got away from all that.)

The *transliterations* in this book are not uniform; nor do I see any good reason why they should be. Uniformity in rendering the sounds of a foreign language is possible only by means of an international phonetic alphabet. Every now and then a translator thinks he can solve the problem his own way; but sooner or later, as when he finds himself spelling "Khrushchev" "Hrooshchyoff" (admittedly closer phonetically: But who would recognize it?) he gives up. Here and there in the poems, when it seemed important to render the sound of a word as closely as possible, I have used such spellings as (for instance) "Alyona" for "Alena." For the same reason I have used the spelling "tsar" in "Kalashnikov" and other poems. But I have made no attempt to harmonize these transliterations with the rest of the *Reader's* text, preferring to leave everything in a pleasantly chaotic state. (Because *really*, when you *get right down to it,* if you don't know Russian pronunciation it just doesn't matter.)

Certain very familiar (in that day—and some of them even now) *Russian forms of address* have been left in the original; e.g., *sudar* ("sir," more or less), *mat' moya* (literally: "Mother mine"—but that's not quite it), and *batyushka* (of all Russian appellations, the most abused by translators). For the reader who protests that these things work a hardship on him, I have no sympathy: he should be glad of the opportunity to learn. Indeed, the *only way* to acquire a feeling for what *batyushka* "means" is to experience it in many different contexts: there is simply no dictionary equivalent, or equivalents. (Anglo-Americans don't think in terms of *batyushka*: they think in terms of "boss," "daddy," and so on.)

The *formal aspects of the poems* (to move, now, to a loftier plane) have been duly respected in most cases: meter always, and rhyme most of the time. The former presents no great problem, since Russian, like English, is an "accentual" language that has made a compromise with syllabic prosody. (*It is in fact closer to English, as a medium for poetry, than any other major language but German.* And in some respects—e.g., the high incidence of slurred unstressed vowels—it is even closer than German.) This is not to say, of course, that Russian stress patterns identically with English: there are a couple of important differences *within* the common framework; and I suspect we shall have to discuss at least one of them when we get to the next consideration: rhyme.

Russian is a highly-inflected language; and from this fact flow consequences of great import to the translator. In such a language (as any student of Latin knows) it is possible to achieve some very "nice" effects via inversions that can be (and often have been) repulsively artificial in an "analytical" language like English. Lermontov, however, was disinclined to follow his master, Pushkin, in exploiting effects of this kind—which makes things easier for both of us, dear reader. But he could not very well eliminate the other major consequence of Russian flexion; namely, that rhyme in Russian—and most especially feminine, dactylic, and hyperdactylic—*is much less emphatic* than in English, because it so often involves flexional segments of words (case-endings, etc.) that have little "semantic weight."

This state of affairs is of course familiar to translators of, say, Italian poetry. T. S. Eliot, for example, when adapting a passage of Dante for "Little Gidding," decided that English rhyme was much too emphatic for the "lightness" of Dante's "chimes," and so settled upon unrhymed alternate masculine and feminine endings. Another excellent reason for the general avoidance of *exact* feminine rhymes in English is that they always contain a suggestion of the burlesque. And when the rhyme is elongated to a dactyl or hyperdactyl—which in Russian are perfectly sober and respectable—the urge to guffaw, on the part of the English reader, is quite irrepressible.

As if this situation weren't bad enough, we must now face up to the additional fact that feminine (or longer) rhymes in Russian are even "lighter" than in Italian or

Spanish—the reason being that when Russian stress is weak it is *very weak indeed*. (Stress in Russian, like the characters in Dostoyevsky, tends to oscillate between the two extremes of bold self-assertion and unprotesting submission to authority.) *

What's to do? My own solution (relatively new in the englishing of Russian poetry, but standard practice among good translators of Spanish and Italian verse) is simply to make liberal use of slant-rhymes, assonance, etc., thereby killing two birds with one stone; viz., gaining greater freedom for myself in following the sense of the original and, at the same time, avoiding the inordinate emphasis (not to mention the burlesque effects) of exact feminine rhymes in English.

Finally, in most of Lermontov's poems written in dactyls (e.g., "Clouds," "The Captive Knight") I have pretty much avoided rhyme effects altogether. This I did for the reasons mentioned above, plus one other. Russian stress does not, like English (American), "pattern binarily." That is, the ratio between strong and weak stress is not in the vicinity of one-to-one, but actually about *one-to-two*. Among the many far-reaching consequences of this fact—especially when conjoined with the aforementioned phenomenon of extreme debility in all unstressed Russian syllables—*is the ease with which Russian speech pat-*

---

* English, by contrast, is rich in intermediate degrees of stress: the weak phonemes, instead of accepting their condition docilely, keep struggling to become middle class, as it were. That English stress can be adequately described only in terms of *four degrees* has been demonstrated by Trager and Smith (*An Outline of English Structure*), with further development in Epstein and Hawkes (*Linguistics and English Prosody*).

terns fit into dactylic and other ternary meters. (For a Russian poet, dactyls are as "normal" as iambs for an English poet.) So great, in fact, is this ease—so "natural" the movement of a Russian poem in ternary meter—that one is entirely carried away by it and scarcely notices the rhymes at all. I therefore decided to omit rhyme altogether from my English versions, choosing to rely entirely upon the "surging movement" that, as I fondly hope, they possess.

So much for my slight deviations from the formal patterns of the originals which, however they may have suffered, would have suffered more from a strict insistence upon exact feminine rhymes, and suchlike.

The texts used as a basis for this *Reader* were: the late Boris Eichenbaum's last four-volume edition, *Polnoe sobranie sochineniy* (Moscow: OGIZ, 1948) and the four-volume *Sobranie sochineniy* edited by I. L. Andronikov, D. D. Blagoy, and Yu. G. Oksman (Moscow: OGIZ, 1957). Various other editions, both pre- and post-revolutionary, were consulted on this or that point of textology.

A LERMONTOV READER

The Tambóv Treasurer's Wife

>	*In a letter to Marya Lopukhina * dated Febru-
ary 15, 1838, Lermontov mentioned in passing:*
>
>	I went to see Zhukovsky and took him "The
Tambóv Treasurer's Wife," which he had asked to
see, and which he then took to Vyazemsky so they
could read it together. They liked it very much,
and it will be published in the next issue of The
Contemporary.†
>
>	*When the poem appeared in print later that year
—anonymously, since Lermontov was still under
official suspicion (see Introduction)—it had been
badly mangled by the censor. (I. I. Panayev, in his
Literary Reminiscences, reports that Lermontov
flew into a rage when he saw it.) Some lines were
deleted entirely; and since the original MS. was
lost, it has never been possible to restore them with
certainty. In this edition, those lines are indicated
by ellipses. Lines enclosed by brackets represent
questionable restorations used by P. A. Viskovatov
in his edition of Lermontov's* Works *(1889–1891).*
>	—Ed.

>	*Gamble, but don't lose your head and shirt.*
>	**PROVERB**

---

* The older sister of Varvara Lopukhina, the poet's love and the life
model for Princess Ligovskaya in the novel of the same name.

† *Sovremmenik*, the magazine edited by Pushkin until his death the
year before. Like the more eminent Zhukovsky, Prince Pyotr Andreyevich
Vyazemsky (1792–1878), poet and critic, was a close friend of Pushkin.

DEDICATION

Let people say that I'm old-fashioned: [1]
I'm not disturbed—I'll even smile;
I use the rhythms of *Onegin;*
I sing, my friends, in the old style.
Please listen to this little story.
Perhaps, when you have thought it over,
You'll nod approval and commend
Its strange and unexpected end.
According to the ancient practice,
We'll drink a fortifying wine
To wash down our uneven lines;
And, limping, they will follow after
Their docile kin, and come to rest
At the River of Forgetfulness.

I

Time was, Tambóv was not distinguished
By a circle on the map: disgrace [2]
Was once in fact its formal standing;
But now, of course, it's quite a place.
It has three straight streets, with all paving—
And streetlamps—and a pair of taverns,
One of them called The Moscow Inn,
The other simply, The Berlin.
Besides, it has four sentry boxes
With two sentries in front of each;
They all salute quite properly

[1] (Old Believer) A member of the schismatic group of the Russian Orthodox Church, persecuted for clinging to the older ritual after Nikon's Reform of 1652. By Lermontov's time the word was generally used in the sense of "old-fashioned."

[2] In the eighteenth century, Tambóv was among those places designated as "objects of the Imperial disfavor"; i.e., a kind of "Siberia closer to home."

And, twice a day, relieve the watches.
[The jail's the best for miles around]
In short, a splendid little town.

II

But boredom! God! It's just as boring
There, as in Petersburg. They brew
Their drinks out of a tasteless poison;
They lay their calloused hands on you.
The town is full of pompous dandies:
Experts on manners—all pedantic;
And there's no chance to get away
From fools and musical *soirées*.
And you should see the local ladies!
Austere Dianas in mobcaps,
With "No!" forever on their lips.
The surest way to get to Hades
Is to think evil when with them:
They read your thoughts, and you're condemned!

III

One day a tremor shook the nobles
And quite transformed the maidens fair:
A dragoon outfit was reported
En route to spend the winter there.
Dragoons! Ah! Splendid fellows! Very
Likely the colonel isn't married;
And naturally, the general
Will want to give a brilliant ball.
The mothers' eyes gleamed with elation;

Whereas the fathers, who were all
Horrible misers, were appalled
As they reflected: spurs and sabers
Are bad for newly-lacquered floors . . .
Tambóv was in a small uproar.

And then, one morning just at daybreak
(The hour that's best for virgins' dreams)
When, through the heavy mist that veils it,
The River Tsna is scarcely seen,
When dawn's first rays have richly gilded
The highest domes of the cathedral,
And that notorious foe of peace,
The alehouse, slumbers quietly,

.   .   .   .

.   .   .   .

Dragoons by sixes, on the right,
Entered the town; while the musicians,
Who'd sat their mounts asleep till then,
Struck up the march from *Two Blind Men*.[3]

v

Who wouldn't feel his heart beat wildly
When first he heard the tender neighs
Of those black horses, whose arrival
Had been devoutly sought for days?
Warm featherbeds are left behind, now.

[3] *Les Deux aveugles de Toléde,* an opera by the French composer
Etienne-Nicolas Méhule (1763–1817).

"*Maláshka*! (Stupid!) Kátya, mind now,
Bring me my slippers and my shawl.
And where is Ivan? What a fool!
Two years to get the shutters open!"
Now, shuttters wide, with might and main
All hands wield rags on dirty panes.
And, curiously, with eyes still swollen
From sleep, the girls survey the lines
Of rough-hewn faces, thick with grime.

VI

"Oh! Just look over this way, Cousin!
At that one!" "Where? The major?" "No . . .
How handsome! And his horse—just stunning!
He's only a lieutenant, though.
Too bad . . . But how he rides—so easily!
I dreamed of him, would you believe it?
Then afterwards I couldn't rest . . ."
And now the maidenly young breast
Swells softly underneath her kerchief;
Remembering her dream, she sighs,
And softness dims her sparkling eyes.
The regiment has passed, now; hurtling
Behind it come the little boys:
Barefooted, dirty, and all noise.

VII

Across the street from the Moskovsky
Inn, where the dragoons had their lair,
There lived a fellow named Bobkovsky,

The old provincial treasurer.
His house, built in the ancient manner,
Was ugly—but then it was tranquil.
Between two peeling colonnades
There drooped a kind of balustrade;
The roof was made of boards, all splintered,
With green moss growing on the wood.
Before the windows, though, there stood
Four flourishing and well-pruned birches:
Instead of curtains and thick blinds,
Adornments of a simpler kind.

VIII

The master was an old man, gloomy,
With a massive head so bald it shone.
From early youth he'd been consuming
The Treasury's money as his own.
He found it pleasurable to roam in
The dark abysses of accounting;
And for this reason he went in
For gambling (it was his one sin).
He dearly loved, on winter evenings,
To deal the cards to right and left,
To cross out his most recent bet,
And boldly stake his total winnings;
Or, when his cards gave him some pain,
To gulp Tsimlyánskaya champagne.[4]

---

[4] So called after Tsimlyánskaya Station, on the Don River.

IX

He was the foe of useful labors,
The spokesman of the sporty ones,
The terror of the local matrons,
And the special tutor of their sons.
Time and again, a farmer's proceeds
From turkeys, oats, and other produce
Were gobbled up in one half-hour
By his marked cards. His cronies were
The police inspector, judge, and doctor.
The first dined often at the house
With the treasurer and his young spouse.
His waggish jesting sometimes shocked her
At the dinner table, so that she
Would have to blush most prettily.

X

One thing I see I didn't mention:
Our treasurer lived a married life.
His Maker blessed him when he sent him
A perfect jewel of a wife.
He rated her as something precious,
But never spent much on her dresses,
And never sent for beautiful
New bonnets from the capital.
He taught her secrets of his know-how:
The use of languid looks and sighs
So some enamored player's eyes
Would fail to catch a quick maneuver.

Meantime, the sharp old reprobate
Watched every move his young wife made.

XI

Truly, Avdótya Nikolávna
Was a dainty dish. She moved around
Proudly, and with a flowing motion,
Her slippers scarcely touching ground.
Tambovians could not remember
Another breast so high, so tender
(Its every vein was visible),
So white (like sugar), and so full.
It seemed as if she'd been created
For tender passions. And her eyes?
Like turquoise, or Italian skies.
But I admit I have my favorites
(I worship eyes of azure blue)
So I can't hope to judge for you.

XII

That little nose! Those lips—so pretty!
Like fresh rose petals! Teeth that seemed
To have been fashioned out of pearl shell;
And a voice as sweet as any dream.
She had some trouble (the poor dearie)
With 'r's: she couldn't say them clearly.
But who would not forgive, in her,
A tiny blemish like a burr?
Her aged spouse, in tender moments,
Would often give her cheek a pat.

It really was a pity that
They had no children . . .

. . . .

. . . .

XIII

To clarify my story further,
It's time that I explained to you:
Avdótya's sister had just fallen
Madly in love with a dragoon.
And she (as one should) kept her secret
By telling Dúnya [5] it was secret.
Now, did you ever chance to hear
A talk between two sisters dear,
Both married? O great God in Heaven!
The things those darling lips can say!
O wondrous Russian naïveté!
Believe me, I'm a truthful fellow;
And from behind the folding screens
(Two different times) I heard *such* things. . . .

XIV

So, in this way, the local beauty
Learned to appreciate dragoons.

. . . .

. . . .

What then? Knowledge was what undid her.
A dragoon, something of a kidder

[5] Another diminutive for Avdótya's baptismal name, Yevdókiya (Eudoxia).

(I'd spent a lot of time with him)
Was staying at the Moscow Inn
In a room whose window faced her window.
He wore a captain's epaulettes.
At thirty, slim as a cadet;
Mustache quite black; eyes that could kindle
Passion, and make a virgin sigh:
In short, a splendid Russian type.

X V

While still an ensign, he had wasted
His father's whole estate; since then,
Like one of God's birds, he'd subsisted
Upon the gifts of Providence.
He often went to bed not knowing
What he might find to eat next morning.
He'd covered Russia, sea to sea:
As courier, in the cavalry,
Sometimes (half-drunk) convoying horses,
Sometimes on leave, philandering:
He had grown used to all these things.
I might have thought that all his stories
Were bluff, if I had ever heard
One trace of bragging in his words.

X V I

Since earthly passions never swayed him,
He never lost his savoir-faire.
[And Heaven itself would not have fazed him
If he had chanced to end up there.]

In battle, when grapeshot was rattling,
He could start everybody laughing
With pompous speeches, vulgar skits,
Awful grimaces, and sheer wit.
For sport, once, in an altercation,
He'd shot a good friend in the head;
For sport he'd make a grave his bed,
Or start a minor revolution.
He could be gentle as a child:
A good man, but a little wild.

XVII

He didn't fit the usual pattern
For what we call a gigolo;
He never took the beaten pathway,
Since he could beat one of his own.
He wasn't one for declarations
Of passion, or for supplications
On bended knee. And yet the sly
Boy had more luck than you or I.

. . . .
. . . .
. . . .

Such was our hero, Captain Garin.
At any rate this portrait shows
What he was like five years ago.

XVIII

He soon learned from the tavernkeeper
The things worth knowing in Tambóv:

A good half-dozen secret intrigues
(Really quite funny); how well off
The debutantes were; and what hangouts
The marriage brokers were now haunting.
But most of all, his troubled thoughts
Were full of what he'd heard about
The treasurer's wife—his fair young neighbor.
"Poor little thing!" thought the dragoon.
"Does that old, doddering buffoon
Have any right to keep you caged there
Under his guard, while I just wait—
A churl, unmoved by your sad fate?"

XIX

He acted fast. Soon he was seated
At the window, in his Persian robe,
While from his fancy pipe, glass-beaded,
Small, dainty wisps of smoke arose.
A skullcap of cerise, with golden
Trimming (for which he was beholden
To a certain young Moldavian girl)
Was perched atop his soft, dark curls.
He sat, and diligently waited.
Then, like a form seen through a mist,
Against the windowpane he glimpsed
The profiled head of his dear neighbor.
He heard a sharp rap from inside
The window; then it was flung wide.

XX

The town is still asleep and tranquil;
Windows reflect the morning sun;
There is, as yet, no lively clatter
Of carriage wheels on cobblestones.
What is the treasurer's young wife doing
Up and around so soon this morning?
What can the actual reason be?
Insomnia? Quite possibly.
Her chin cupped in her right hand, pensive,
She sighs. In her left hand she's got
A sock. But we'll ignore the sock:
To dwell on it would be offensive.
Yet, frankly, I would like to know:
For her, is darning apropos?

XXI

At first she fixed her charming eyes on
The vault of heaven; then her gaze
Swept down the skies toward the horizon,
And suddenly—what a disgrace!
Across the street, right in the window,
Sans uniform, a *man* was sitting!
Your frockcoat, captain! Get it—quick!
As he deserved, the window clicked
Shut, and the lovely vision ended.
Of course, dear readers, such a sad
Event might very well just add
To your confusion. But I'll render

A smart salute to our dragoon:
He murmured, "So! Things have begun!"

XXII

For two whole days she didn't open
Her window. He was patient. Then,
The third day, her enchanting profile
Once more appeared against the pane.
The sash squeaked gently. With her mending
In hand, she sat down at the window.
But his experienced eye assessed
How very carefully she was dressed.
So, satisfied with his achievement,
He left his post, and stayed away
Till morning of the following day.
And then, although the pain was grievous,
He used what will he had in store
And stayed away for three days more.

XXIII

But this first, petty quarrel was fated
To run the course of lovers' quarrels:
The pair had soon elaborated
A language—mute, but meaningful.
Language of love, marvelous language,
One that is known to young hearts only,
To whom, though he be loved but once,
Have you not been a mother tongue?
In moments of tumultuous passion,
Whom have you not helped, once at least,

When close embraced, or at her feet?
Whom, in the fetters of coercion,
Amid the spiteful, vicious throng,
Have you not saved, O wondrous tongue!

XXIV

I'll make it brief: from two weeks' watching,
Our Garin knew by heart just when
She got up, took tea with her husband,
And went out for her walk. And then,
If she was going to morning service,
Garin would be there bright and early.
He'd stand, leaning against the wall,
And never cross himself at all.
The ikon lamps, meanwhile, were casting
A reddish glow upon his face:
How bleak and glowering it was!
But all the while his probing glances
(First bright, then dim, by fits and starts)
Were trying to penetrate her heart.

XXV

The curiosity of women
Is well known, from both life and books:
The dragoon made a great impression
On Dunya, just by his strange looks.
Of course, it wasn't good behavior
To pave the way into her favor
With sinful thoughts—the kind we fear,
And yet (somehow) hold very dear!

. . . .
. . . .
. . . .

Life without love is so revolting!
And how can gray-haired husbands be
Objects of passion? You tell me.

XXVI

But time went by. "Come on. Let's hurry!"
Spoke up our much-enamored male.
"This wordless sighing is for stories;
But I'm no hero of a tale."
One day a lackey entered, making
A low, deep bow. "What's this?" "A message.
My master sends respects to you.
He couldn't come himself—he's too
Busy. He says, sir, you're invited
To dine, with dancing afterwards.
Those were the master's very words."
"Well, run along. Say I'm delighted."
And at three sharp, donning his fine
Jacket, the captain went to dine.

XXVII

Amphytrion, dean of the gentry,[6]
Was strict about propriety:
To fête his wife, he had assembled
The top ranks of society

[6] The *predvoditel'* (*"maréchal de la noblesse"*) was social leader of the local gentry.

And all the regiment together.
The general made all the others
Wait for him, and then yawned all day;
But the party went well anyway.
It had been set up very nicely:
On tables stood deep vases full
Of apples for the womenfolk;
And for the men, upon the sideboard,
Were three large cases of good wine
Which just that morning had arrived.

XXVIII

The host, accompanied by the general's
Lady, went in to dinner. When
The beautiful but modest gender
Were seated (not too near the men),
From the balcony, above the clatter
Of knives and spoons on plates and platters,
The entire section of dragoons'
Trumpets blared forth in unison.
A usage old but advantageous:
It stimulates the appetite,
And may conveniently drown out
Amorous words between two neighbors.
But in the present age we're told
To laugh at everything that's old.

XXIX

Today, you won't find any traces
Of the boyards' customs, or their breed;

Only at hussars' celebrations
Do trumpets blare as they once did.
O when will I again be sitting
Among old friends—our goblets brimming
With wine—and hearing, all night long,
The rousing regimental songs?
When will I see the deep red splendor
Of fur-trimmed cloaks, in that gray hour
When on the straight ranks of hussars
(Still half-asleep), and on the tents there
Among the trees, the new dawn casts,
Stealthily, its first gleaming shafts?

XXX

Beside Avdótya Nikolávna
The daring captain took his place.
He twirled his long mustache gallantly,
And fixed her with a stubborn gaze.
He noticed that her pulse had quickened . . .
And then (I don't know how it happened)
He lightly brushed his spur against
Her foot or slipper. Then commenced
The excuses, and a conversation
Began. One compliment apiece,
A tender glance, and they had reached
The stage of passionate declarations.
Yes, yes—an honorable officer.
But Mrs. Treasurer—what of her?

XXXI

Quickly concealing her mute raptures,
She offered him the irksome trial
(In answer to his tender whispers)
Of friendship pure and undefiled.
Such are the manners of the rustics!
And women love to make us suffer.
But we know all too much of love
Between friends, and the friendship of
The ladies! What a hellish torment
To sit all evening, tête-à-tête
With a pretty girl, not nineteen yet,

.   .   .   .

.   .   .   .

.   .   .   .

XXXII

In recent years, among the maidens
Of our large cities, I've observed
A passion for ethereal madness
And mysticism. Beware them, sirs!
Just when you've got some time for loving,
These female devotees of learning
Will suddenly want to prove to you
That one plus one can't equal two.
Or else, instead of hot embraces,
They'll give you Mesmerism. A man
Is lucky if he's put in trance.
The fruits of all such observations

Must be kept secret, naturally.
But *my* aim is utility.

XXXIII

I won't describe the ball, dear reader,
Although it was a brilliant one;
But I will say that all that evening
Eros was helping our dragoon.
Alas! [Now, other gods revering,]
People no longer worship Eros.
Forgotten is love's fairy prince:
His altar has grown cold long since.
Provincials, though, aren't quick to follow
The city folks' enlightenment.

. . . .
. . . .
. . . .

XXXIV

His powerful gaze had conquered Dúnya,
And fettered that poor heart of hers.
The whole night long she kept on dreaming
Of rattling swords and jangling spurs.
And when, next day, having arisen
At nine, she sat down with her knitting
In a rumpled robe, the selfsame dream
Continued as a revery.
Her jealous spouse was at his office.
She was alone, dreaming like mad.
Suddenly, she heard a knock. "Who's that?

Andryushka? Oh! You lazy ox, you!"
She heard footsteps. And then a face
Appeared . . . but it was not Andrei's.

XXXV

Of course you've already discovered
This sudden guest's identity.
It may be that our bold young lover
Was acting somewhat hastily.
But still, considering his patience
In the past, and then deliberating
I'm sure you'll think it not amiss
That our young man should run this risk.
Bowing his head, he very quickly
Approached Dúnya. Without a word,
He stood and simply stared at her,
His gaze forlorn, bedimmed, and sickly.
At last he twisted his long, sleek
Mustache, sighed, and began to speak.

XXXVI

"You weren't expecting me—I see it
In your two eyes. Ah! You don't know
How much one hour, even one minute,
Can mean to one in passion's throes!
A heart beset by agitation
Leaves one no strength, control, or patience.
I'm here. I'll go to all extremes.
I'm yours; you're mine. The petty, mean
Things people say will never scare me,

And nothing else will. I defy
Society's gossip. Either I
Will go and shoot myself (I swear it!)—
Oh! Don't be frightened. Please don't shake!
Tell me you love me. Speak! Oh, speak!"

XXXVII

He stood and looked down at her, feigning
Humility. His gaze burned low
At first; then, kindled by his flaming
Passion, it took a red-hot glow.
All pale and quite confused, poor Dúnya
Sat still. It seemed to him that soon, now,
The sweet fruits of love's victory
Would be his own . . . but suddenly
An unexpected and unwitting
Shyness engulfed her soul. She blushed
All over, and with one hand thrust
Him off. "Enough! I will not listen
To any more! If you don't leave
Right now—I'm telling you—I'll scream!"

XXXVIII

He studied her: she meant it—really.
Look at it any way you please,
This was plain, ordinary female
Obstinacy. Damn such caprice!
And then—Oh, height of degradation!—
He had recourse to supplication
On bended knee. But as he did,

The door was opened, and there stood
Her husband. "Oh!" The two men traded
Fierce glances. But the dark storm clouds
Were dissipated without words,
And Garin left. At home he readied
Pistol and bullets for the duel,
Then sat and smoked his pipe, quite cool.

XXXIX

Within the hour, a servant brought him
A greasy note. *What?* Saints above!
An invitation from Bobkovsky
To a whist party in honor of
His name day. Others are expected. . . .
So thunderstruck, so apoplectic,
Was Garin, that he nearly choked.
Could this be some kind of a joke?
All day our hero was excited.
At last it grew dark. He looked out
The window. What a rogue! The house
Was full of guests, and brightly lighted.
The question was: Should he replace
Pistol in pocket, just in case?

XL

Arriving, he came face to face with
Dúnya herself, with downcast eyes.
Their scarcely started conversation
Was cut short by a heavy sigh.
They both ignored the scene that morning,

And talked like strangers. To his boring
Remarks about the weather, she
Said only, "Uhmm," or, "Yes, I see."
Secretly burning with frustration,
He went into the master's den.
But *we* don't have to rush on in.
Besides, one never should be hasty.
And so, let's take a breather now;
And then we'll finish up somehow.

XLI

Time was, I courted thrills, excitement:
To live intensely was my aim.
With foolish carelessness I slighted
Nature's wise laws. What ever came
Of it? It was absurd, pathetic!
Weariness had my soul in fetters.
I kept on brooding, night and day,
Over the past. To what avail?
The past can never be recovered.
The eagle, eying from his cage,
Mountains and valleys, does not raise
His wings in vain. Without once touching
His blood-soaked food, he sits in calm
Silence, and waits for death to come.

XLII

Then are you gone, O years I treasured,
When everything spoke to the heart,

Which beat in wondrous, powerful measure—
When rapture filled my every thought?
Not always will the eagle languish
Hopelessly, in his cage of iron.
He'll find again that lofty way
He traveled in his younger days,
Where mountain peaks, immense and somber,
Are clad in silvery snow and mist;
Where only eagles dare to nest;
Where caravans of white clouds wander.
There, in that free and sumptuous sky,
He'll spread his wings again, and fly!

XLIII

But all things must end sometime, even
Those high-flown fancies we love most.
So, back to work. Garin has entered
The den. Lo and behold! The host
Welcomes our hero warmly, seats him,
Serves up champagne and, meanwhile, treats him
To jams and jellies. The dragoon
Thinks to himself, "A Judas!" Soon
A crowd of guests is huddled closely
Around a table, chattering:
The game of whist is in full swing.
The treasurer himself is holding
The stakes—for he's a thoughtful man,
Obliging others when he can.

XLIV

Now, since the host himself is busy
With great affairs, it's up to me
To introduce this small but brilliant
Set of Tambóv society.
First comes the counselor: defender
Of morals, and a hound for slander
[For gold he'll gladly prostitute
His conscience, and the law to boot.]
Next comes the district social leader:
Long tail coat, chin hid by his tie,
Shrill voice, mustache, and vacant eye.
The police inspector, jealous keeper
Of order, was there too. But then
You heard about him way back when.

XLV

And next, in half-tails, drenched in perfume,
Slovenly and illiterate,
The modern Mitrofan [7] in person:
A big, immoral idiot.
He had complete faith in the wisdom
Of the treasurer, who would advise him
On placing bets. He thought it quite
An honor, and he bet just right.
The others present . . . but that's plenty.
Dear reader, you have had enough.
Besides, my story's all mixed up.

[7] The archetype of the "Big Booby" and "Mamma's Boy"—after the chief character in Fonvizin's comedy, *The Minor* (or *The Hobbledehoy*).

Against my will, my pen has led me
Into capricious scribbling:
I've said God knows what kind of thing.

XLVI

The game went on. One guest abruptly
Went pale, tore up his cards, and howled.
Another, stunned by his bankruptcy,
Just sat there with his sad head bowed.
Others, whose cards had turned out lucky,
Refilled their glasses with much chuckling,
And clinked them. But the treasurer sat
In gloomy silence. Beads of sweat
Formed on his shiny pate. He'd wagered
His every kopeck. His poor ears
Were ringing with such words as, "Here's
Ten more." "You're called." Then he went crazy:
He bet and lost his ancient house
Plus fixtures, both inside and out.

XLVII

He lost a droshky and a carriage,
Three horses, two horse-collars, all
His furniture, and Dúnya's earrings.
In short, he was cleaned out. Appalled,
Utterly desperate, and wrathful,
He sat in silence. It was after
Midnight. The candle's flickering flame
Was burning low. Outside, the gray
First light of dawn was faintly streaking

The cloudy sky. Most of the guests
Bethought themselves of needed rest.
But suddenly Bobkovsky, leaping
Erect, requested that they stay
And hear something he had to say.

XLVIII

Gravely, he begged their kind permission
To deal one hand. He'd make one try,
And either win back his possessions,
Or else—"The winner takes my wife!"
Frightful! O horrors! O rank evil!
How had the Treasury been able
To keep this man? The guests all seemed
To have been scalded with live steam.
All but the dragoon kept their places.
He rose, and said with perfect poise:
"A pleasure. Let them make their noise.
We'll play this on a friendly basis.
Just one thing: watch the tricky stuff,
Or else you'll find the going rough!"

XLIX

Imagine, now, this group of players
As they looked then: just visualize
The shades of color in their faces,
Their gleaming spectacles and eyes.
First, our mustachioed young lover,
Who plays erect. Then, on the other
Side of the table, framed by two

Candles, a huge head with a few
Gray tufts of hair, quite sparsely scattered;
A mouth straining to smile; a pair
Of hands holding the cards—and there
You'd have the whole scene, if we added
An armchair, just off to one side,
And in it, Bobkovsky's young bride.

L

I dare not tell you at this moment
What feelings stirred inside of her.
Her face expressed so many torments
That, if you knew just what they were,
You might give in to your own feelings
And break out in a fit of weeping.
But may your eyes never be dimmed
By tears of pity. For to him
Who knows life and the world, compassion
Is foolish. The last century
Was sentimental: tales of griefs
And woes that were the purest fictions,
Brought floods of tears. The question is:
Who profited from all of this?

LI

The battle was a fairly short one:
Garin played boldly, and with luck.
As for the old man, fickle Fortune
Just laughed. He lost. His hour had struck.
Avdótya Nikolávna, rising,

Approached the group of men in silence
With gliding step, unhurriedly.
Her forehead, though, was frightfully
Pallid. The stunned guests were predicting
The worst. What would they hear from her?
Complaints? Reproaches? Sobs? No, sir!
She just took off her ring and, fixing
Her husband with a steady gaze,
She flung it straight into his face.

LII

And then she swooned. But Garin grabbed her;
And, leaving everything—his fur
Shako, saber, and scores unadded—
He headed straight for home with her.
Next day, the news caused consternation
Among that moral population.
All week they talked of the affair:
Some jokingly, some with an air
Of gravity. While men defended
The part played by the old buffoon,
The fair sex damned our nice dragoon.
Why, I don't know. Could they have envied
Dúnya perhaps? Oh, no, no, no!
I'm not a slanderer, you know.

LIII

And that's the end of my sad story—
Which, strictly speaking, isn't true.
Now tell me: Did you find it boring?

Did you want passions—action, too?
Today, they're all looking for dramas:
They all want blood—even the mammas.
But like a timid boy, I stopped
Short, just when things were getting hot.
I clumsily brought down the curtain
With just a simple nervous faint.
I didn't have the rivals fight
And then make up, as is the custom.
Too bad. My story's at an end.
That's all you're going to get, my friends.

(1837/38)

A Fairy-Tale for Children

PREFATORY NOTE

> *This poem is a fragment (only twenty-seven stanzas were completed) but an important one: stylistically, and also because it satirizes Lermontov's own gorgeous but operatic "oriental tale," "The Demon." It was written in late 1839 and/or in 1840, the same year in which Lermontov finally laid aside "The Demon," having struggled with it, through a total of eight drafts, beginning eleven years earlier.* —ED.

The age of epic poems has passed away,
And tales in verse are terribly neglected.
The poets aren't entirely to blame
(Though some use rhythms they've not quite
   perfected):
The public, too, is guilty in its way.
Now, I don't know who's right and who is wrong here,
But I just don't read poems any longer.
Not, certainly, because I don't love verse;
But why waste time on pretty-sounding words,
When time is money? In this Age of Wisdom
(As you well know), we're all busy with business.

I don't read poems; but, just to regale
Myself, I love to scribble reams of nonsense.

I seize my verses boldly by the tail;
I'm crazy about triple assonances
And liquid rhymes—in, for example, *ale.*
That's why I'm telling you this little story.
In order to ward off all kinds of queries,
I shall avoid explaining, at this point,
Its magical, mysterious dénouement.
It will, however, have a moral: I need it,
So that even a little child can read it.

My hero's well known, and my theme not new.
It's better so! New things are fast outdated.
At one time, burning with the flame of youth,
I sang about another kind of demon:
Those were the childish ravings of a fool!
But God knows where the manuscript I treasured
Is now: Is someone's dainty, gloved hand turning
Its pages, while a voice asks, *"C'est joli?"*
Or is a mouse nibbling it busily? . . .
This devil, though, is different altogether—
An aristocrat, and quite unlike a devil.

I ask you now to come with me into
A girl's bedroom: the rose blinds have been lowered;
Your eyes can just distinguish, through the gloom,
The oriental carpet on the floor.
A pleasant trembling suddenly seizes you:
Intoxicated by the maiden's breathing,
The very air seems heavy with her dreaming.
You see an arm, a shoulder; then, profiled
Against a muslin pillow, you espy

A youthful face—quite stern, but yet endearing.
And at it, Mephistopheles is leering.

Now whether it was Satan there himself,
Or one of those small, lower-ranking goblins
Whose friendship seems to be of such great help
For secret deals in love and family problems,
I just don't know. If only he'd possessed
An earthly shape, by looking at his clothing
And horns, I could have told him from the nobles.
But spirits . . . well, we know what spirits are:
Life, feeling, hearing, vision, voice, and power
Of thought sans body. Their disguises vary:
In paintings, demons generally are scarey.

I haven't always seen in just this form
The Enemy of pure and holy feelings.
My youthful mind was often preyed upon
By a mighty image. Sometimes I would see him
As a proud and ever-silent king, who shone
With such a wondrous sweetness in his splendor,
That I was frightened, and my heart was rended
By a strange anguish . . . this delirium
Obsessed my mind for many years. And then,
Having disowned my other dreams as worthless,
I rid myself of it by means of verses.

[Stanzas I–VI]

(1839/1840)

EARLY LYRICS AND
OTHER SHORT POEMS

(1830–1832)

A Prophecy *

A year will come—for Russia, a black year—
When the crown so many tsars have worn, will fall;
The mob will lose the love it had for them,
And multitudes will feed on blood and death.
The law, thrown over, will no longer shield
The little children and the chaste young wives;
And Plague from stinking bodies of the dead
Will roam the streets of mourning villages,
And silently call victims from their homes;
And Hunger's teeth will tear at this poor land;
And reddening skies will make the rivers red.

On that day will appear a powerful man.
And you will know him, and will understand
Why in his grasp he holds a shining knife.
And woe to you! Your weeping and your groans
Will only make him laugh. And everything
About him will be frightening and dark,
Like his black cloak, beneath his towering brow.

(1830)

* In the margin of the original manuscript of this poem, the sixteen-
year-old poet wrote: "This was a dream."

The Sail

A lone sail makes a patch of whiteness
Against the blue mist on the sea.
What does he seek past far horizons?
And what did he forsake, to flee?

The waves leap up, the wind is freshening,
The mast is laboring, and creaks.
It isn't happiness he flees from,
Alas! Not happiness he seeks.

The bright blue water flows beneath him;
Above, the sun shines—gold and round.
Be he, rebellious, seeks the tempest,
As though in tempests, peace were found!

(1832)

The Angel

An angel was flying through midnight's deep blue,
And softly he sang as he flew;
The moon, and the clouds, and the stars in a throng
All listened: in heavenly song

He sang of the blessings of souls without sin
In the gardens of Paradise; hymns
To God the almighty he sang, and his praise
Was pure and completely unfeigned.

He carried toward earth, with its tears and its grief,
A soul just beginning its life;
And long, long thereafter the soul could still hear
The song he sang—wordless, but clear.

The soul languished long in its worldly attire,
Still knowing a wondrous desire;
And that heavenly music was never usurped
By the wearisome songs of the earth.

(1831)

No, I'm Not Byron

No, I'm not Byron: set apart
Like him, by Fate (though I'm unknown yet),
Like him, I am an exile—homeless;
But in me beats a Russian heart.

I started sooner, I'll end sooner;
But little work will I complete.
Within my soul, as in the ocean,
Cargoes of broken hopes lie deep.

And who can know, O brooding ocean,
Thy many secrets? Who will tell
The mass of men my meditations?
Myself or God—but no one else!

(1832)

To A Young Lady Beautiful But Dumb—I

I'm quite prepared to be enchanted,
Just watching you from far away;
But may I never hear (God grant it!)
A single word that you might say.

Laughter, or fright, or both together,
Would shatter my sweet revery;
And the stupid nothings that you utter
Would quite dispel your witchery.

Thus Death, when she is not close by us,
Is beautiful. Let her run free:
I'll gladly follow her, provided
She doesn't turn and follow me.

I'll follow her where'er she leads me,
And contemplate her night and day;
But not for anything—believe me—
Would I attract her gaze my way!

(1830)

To A Young Lady Beautiful But Dumb—II

Eros once very kindly asked me
To give his vintage wine a try;
I wasn't thirsty, but I thanked him,
And drained the cup till it was dry.

Now, I'd give anything to moisten
My parched and burning lips. Instead,
I find (alas!) the cup of passion
Is empty, like your pretty head.

(1830)

The Blue Mountains of the Caucasus

FRAGMENT

Often at dawn I have looked out at the distant snows
and the ice-sheathed crags: they glittered with such brilliance in the light of the rising sun! And then, as they
began to take a pinkish glow, they would announce, while
all was yet in darkness down below, the coming of the
morning. Their rosy tint was just the color of a blush:
like a young girl who, while in bathing, has been surprised by men, and is confused, so that she fails to cover
her young breasts with her white garment.

How I loved your storms, O Caucasus! Your bleak and
howling storms, to which the caves made answer, like
watchmen of the night! . . . On a barren hill, a single
clump of trees, bent low by rain; or a vineyard rustling
in a deep ravine; an unknown path along the edge of an
abyss, and far below a rushing, foaming river with no
name; a sudden shot, and the terror after the shot: hunter,
or treacherous foe? . . . Everything, yes, everything in this
country is superb.

(1832)

A Song About Tsar Iván Vasíl'yevich, the Young Bodyguard, and the Valorous Merchant Kaláshnikov

PREFATORY NOTE

Written in 1837, shortly after Lermontov's first banishment to the Caucasus, "Kalashnikov" was published anonymously in the spring of 1838. The censors had at first refused categorically to permit the publication of anything from the pen of the recently court-martialed young officer; and it was only through the vigorous intervention of Zhukovsky that "Kalashnikov" was allowed to appear in print.

Lermontov's characterization of Ivan the Terrible ("the Dread," "the Awesome," or whatever) in this poem has been much discussed. The concensus seems to be that it coincides closely with the image of Ivan IV as it developed in the popular imagination. Incidentally, the word 'bodyguard' is only a partial equivalent for the Russian oprichnik, *denoting a member of the* oprichnina *("separate court") set up by Ivan in 1564, which terrorized the country for some years before it was disbanded.*

Rhythmically, "Kalashnikov" is patterned after the commonest features of the bylina, *or folk epic;*

viz., a three-stress line usually ending in a dactylic foot (though it may be hyperdactylic on the one hand, or even iambic on the other) with very irregular stress distribution against which a trochaic internal pattern struggles to assert itself. Thus the first line goes:

Okh ty goy yesí, tsar' Iván Vasíl'yevich!

This is an awkward vehicle (the bylina *line should really be* sung) *and I have striven to reproduce that awkwardness as closely as possible. Exact reproduction is of course impossible, owing to the differences between the nature of stress in Russian and in English* (cf. A Few Technicalities); *e.g., the frequent series of three or four very weak phonemes in the Russian are intolerable to the resiliency of English. Still and all, English can come closer to this kind of accentual verse than any other major language.*
—Ed.

Now all hail to thee, Tsar Iván Vasíl'yevich!
'Tis of thee we have fashioned the song we sing;
Yes, of thee, thy favorite bodyguard,
And the valorous young merchant, Kaláshnikov.
We have fashioned our song in the olden style;
We have sung it while strumming our citharas,
With lamenting, ornamenting it.
All the Orthodox folk have been comforted.
The boyar, good Matvéy Romodánovsky,
Served us mead that did foam in the drinking cup;
And his lady, the fair-faced boyárynya,
Did bring forth, on a tray of fine silverwork,
A newly-woven napkin-cloth, with silk embroidery.

They regaled us for three days, three evenings;
And they listened long, never languishing.

I

It is not the sun so far, shining high above,
Nor are blue-tinted cloudlets admiring him:
At his banquet board doth sit, in his golden crown,
The most Awesome Tsar, Iván Vasíl'yevich.
Just in back of him stand his dopifers,
And across from him are the princes and boyars,
While on either side sit his bodyguards.
The Tsar doth revel now, the Lord to glorify—
For his own good pleasure, too, and his merriment.

With a smile, the Tsar bade a serving man
Fill his golden bowl with a sparkling wine—
Sweet to taste, and from a foreign land—
And then proffer it to the bodyguards.
All drank deeply, loudly praising him.

Only one of them, of the bodyguards,
A most fearless wight, ever quick to fight,
Did not wet his lips in the golden bowl.
His dark eyes were downcast, never glancing up;
And his head drooped heavily on his mighty breast;
And within that breast dwelt a dark despondency.

Then his Sovereign, frowning angrily,
Fixed his sharp-sighted eyes on the younger man,
As a hawk might look down from the heaven's vault
At a poor little pigeon with wings of gray.
But the warrior youth did not look at him.

Then the Awesome Tsar brought his scepter down
In a crashing blow, and its iron tip
Sank a handbreadth or more in the oaken floor.
But the bodyguard still did not flinch at this.
Then at last the Tsar uttered direful words;
And the younger man stirred, and paid heed to him.

"Eh thou vassal good and true, Kiribéyevich!
Art thou harboring a thought of an evil kind?
Does our glory make thee to envy us?
Has thy honorable service grown wearisome?
When the moon arises, the stars are gladdened thereby,
For their heavenly paths are better lighted.
But the star that would seek to hide himself
In a cloud, falls earthward, plummeting.
Most unseemly 'tis that thou, Kiribéyevich,
Scorn'st the reveling of thy Sovereign.
For the blood in thy veins is Skurátov blood;
Thou wert bred in Malyuta's own family." [1]

Kiribéyevich thus made answer then
To the Awesome One, bowing reverently:

"O my liege and lord, Iván Vasíl'yevich!
Do not censure thy slave, an unworthy one!
For a heart on fire is not damped with wine,
Nor are brooding thoughts eased by merriment.
If thy wrath I have provoked, let thy will be done:
Have me put to death—have my head cut off.
It hangs heavily on these brawny shoulders, Sire,

[1] Malyuta Skuratov—"the notoriously cruel head of Ivan's *oprichniki*."
(Gleb Struve)

And doth weigh toward mother earth of its own
accord."

In this wise replied Tsar Iván Vasíl'yevich:
"But what is it then, gallant lad, thou grievest for?
Has the fine brocade of thy long cloak worn thin?
Has thy sable-trimmed cap lost all its shapeliness?
Hast thou squandered all the gold in thy treasure
hoard?
Hast thou nicked the edge of thy tempered saber
blade?
Or wast knocked from thy feet by a trading man's son
While at fisticuffs on Moskvá-Reká?" [2]

Kiribéyevich thus replied to him,
With a shake of his head and his curly locks:

"No man living has an arm of such magic puissance,
Either 'mongst the boyars, or the merchant class.
My swift thoroughbred steed gallops easily;
As a mirror bright, gleams my keen-edged blade;
And on festival days, thanks to thee, my lord,
My attire is the equal of any man's.
When along the far bank of Moskvá-Reká
On my frisky steed I go galloping,
'Round my waist is bound tightly a silken sash;
And my rich velvet cap, with its sable trimming,
I wear jauntily, at a rakish angle.
At the wooden gates, made of slender planks,
Stand the pretty maids, and young matrons, too.

[2] In the wintertime, the "boxing matches" sponsored by Ivan IV were
held on the iced-over Moscow River ("Moskvá-Reká").

They admire me, and trade whispered words about me.
Only one never looks or admires me,
But instead hides her face in her stripèd veil.

"In all Holy Rus', our dear motherland,
Thou may'st seek, but shan't find another fair as she.
Smooth her gait is, as of the gliding swan;
Soft her gaze is, as the turtledove's;
Sweet her voice is, as the nightingale's.
The warm flush in her cheeks is a rosy red,
As when dawn first tinges morning skies.
And her flaxen braids, glinting goldenly,
Plaited prettily with bright ribbon-bands,
To her shoulders fall, where they twine about
And do seem to kiss her snowy breast.
She is of a family of the merchant class,
And her name is Alyóna Dmítrevna.

"When I recognize her, I am not myself;
These strong arms of mine dangle listlessly,
And a dimness comes to my sparkling eyes.
Weary, dreary, then, Tsar of the Orthodox,
Seems this sad and lonely life I lead.
No delight to me is a swift-paced steed,
And no pleasure, my garments of fine brocade.
Of no use to me is a treasure hoard.
For with whom should I share all my treasure now?
Before whom should I show off my bravery?
And to whom should I boast of my finery?

"Give me leave to go off to the Volga lands—
To a life of liberty, in the Cossack style.

I'll lay down, there, this turbulent head of mine—
Lay it down on the spear of an infidel.
And the impious Tátars will divide the spoils:
My good thoroughbred, and my keen-edged sword,
And my warrior's saddle of Circassian make.
Carrion birds will pluck from me, these sad eyes of
    mine;
Driving rains will beat upon my abandoned bones;
And my wretched dust, with no burial rites,
Will be wafted everywhere by wailing winds."

With a smile, thus spoke Iván Vasíl'yevich:
"Well, our loyal young liege, we will do our best
To relieve thy distress and thy sorrowfulness.
Do thou take, then, this ring set with precious rubies;
And take, also, this necklace of orient pearls.
Pay a call on some clever old matchmaker;
And then send these gifts, so invaluable,
To thy dear Alyóna Dmítrevna.
If she like thee well, hold thy wedding feast.
If she like thee not, be not wroth with her."

All hail to thee, Tsar Iván Vasíl'yevich!
Thy deceitful slave did inveigle thee:
What he said to thee was not Gospel truth;
For he never revealed that the lady fair
Had been duly wed in the Holy Church—
Had been duly wed to a merchant youth,
In accordance with the Christian marriage law.

Ai, my hearties, sing out! But keep your zithers tuned!
Ai, my hearties, drink up! But do your duty, too!

Ye will pleasure the good Romodánovsky
And his lady, the fair-faced boyárynya.

I I

At his shop counter doth sit the young trading man,
A sturdy, handsome lad, Stepán Paramónovich,
With the family name of Kaláshnikov.
His silk stuffs he lays out and scrutinizes,
Coaxing passers-by in tones sweetly supplicating,
As he counts, meanwhile, gold and silver pieces.
But the day has been very bad for him:
Folk of wealth and fashion have sauntered past,
Never noticing his neat shop interior.

All the church bells have sounded for the vespers
    hour.
A dim sunset glows behind the Kremlin walls;
In the heavens, clouds are scurrying,
Driven by the raging of a blizzard wind;
And the great bazaar is quite empty now.
The young merchant, Stepán Paramónovich,
Locks the stout, oaken door of his market stall
With a German padlock with a spring in it;
Then affixes a chain, an iron one,
To a mastiff with fangs long and fearsome-looking.

To deep in thought, he goes home to his youthful
    wife
Far across the river, the Moskvá-Reká.
When he comes at last to his lofty house,
Full amazed is Stepán Paramónovich.

His young wife is not there for his welcoming;
On the oaken table boards, no white cloth is laid;
And the flame of the ikon lamp is scarce flickering.
He rings for the venerable old housekeeper:
"Tell me quickly now, Yereméyevna,
Where has my Alyóna Dmítrevna
Gone to hide herself at such a late hour as this?
And my children so dear—my little ones?
Did they run too hard, or else play too much,
And go straight to bed at an early hour?"

"O good master mine, Stepán Paramónovich!
I will tell thee things that are wondrous strange.
Alyóna Dmitrévna went to hear evensong.
Then the priest came back, his young wife on his arm;
They made light and sat down for the evening meal.
But thy goodwife, sir, even at that late hour,
Still had not come back here from the parish church.
And thy children—precious little things—
Neither sleeping are they, nor gone off to play:
They keep weeping, and won't make an end of it."

Then an ominous thought sore discomfited
The young trading man, Kaláshnikov.
He went to the window and looked out of it.
In the street outside it was darkest night:
Snow fell thick and fast, spreading everywhere,
Filling in the tracks left by human feet.

Then he heard, from the hall, a door closed noisily,
And steps, as of someone who was hurrying.

When he turned, then, and looked—by the Holy
    Saints!
There his young wife stood, right in front of him.
Ghostly pale she was, with her head uncovered;
In her flaxen hair, all unbound and loose,
Beads of frost and snow were still glittering.
Her eyes stared dully, vacantly, like a madwoman's;
From her lips came incoherent whisperings.

"Tell me where, O wife of mine, wast frolicking?
In a private dwelling, or publicly?—
That thy hair is down, and disorderly;
That thy clothing is all ripped and rended so?
Thou wert reveling—yes, and dallying—
With some stripling youths of boyar degree.
Not for this, O my wife, did the two of us
Once exchange golden rings and our marriage vows
Before the holy ikons of the Orthodox!
I will put thee away behind padlocks of iron
On a stout, oaken door with iron mounting.
And the blessed daylight, then, thou shalt never see;
And this honored name I bear, thou shalt not
    besmirch."

When she heard these words, Alyóna Dmítrevna
Trembled fearfully like a poor turtledove,
And did shake like a leaf in the autumn time.
Then most piteously she began to weep,
Kneeling humbly at her husband's feet.

"O my gracious lord, sun that lights my life,

Either kill me now, or else listen to me.
Thy reproaches, like a keen-edged knife,
Rend my heart so, it is like to break.
I fear not a death of violence;
I fear not the things that people say;
What I do fear, is to anger thee.

"I was coming from vespers this very night—
All alone I was, in the darkened street—
And a sound I did hear, as when snow is crunched.
When I turned I saw someone following me.
My poor legs went weak, and refused to move;
And I covered my face with my silken veil.
He laid hold of my arm with his powerful grasp,
And he said to me in a whispered voice:
'Why dost fear me so, prettiest of pretty maids?
No low thief am I, slaying passers-by,
But a faithful liege of the Awesome Tsar.
Kiribéyevich is the name I bear,
And I come from the famous Malyúta's clan.'
Even greater then, did my fright become;
And my foolish little head began to whirl around.
He began to kiss and to fondle me.
As he kissed me, he did repeat these words:
'Only answer me: What is it thou wishest for?
Is it gold thou want'st? Orient pearls, perhaps?
Dost desire brilliant gems or bright-hued brocade?
I'll array thee as in a queen's attire;
Everyone will learn to envy thee.

But let me not, by my own hand, perish sinfully.
Grant thy love to me! Hold me close to thee,
Be it only once, ere I go from thee.'

"Then he kissed me again, and did fondle me.
Even now my cheeks feel the burning heat
Spreading over them like a living flame,
From the damnable kisses he gave to me.
From the doorways the women were watching us;
And they laughed as they pointed their fingers at us.

"Then I tore myself from his grasping hands,
And I ran toward home in a headlong flight.
But I left in the hands of the highwayman
The embroidered shawl that thou gavest me,
And my silken veil, of Bokhara craft.
He has sullied me, and brought shame on me—
On thy honest wife, who was undefiled.
Oh, what will the evil-tongued neighbors say?
And where do I dare, now, to show myself?

"Don't abandon me, thy wife faithful and true,
To the evil tongues who will scoff and jeer.
There is none, except for thee, I can turn to now.
In the world around me, I'm like an orphan child.
My own father lies in the cold, damp earth;
And my mother dear lies beside him there.
I have brethren twain. But the elder one
Disappeared in foreign parts, as thou knowest well.
And the younger one is the merest child—
Just a little boy, far from manhood yet."

Thus to him did speak Alyóna Dmítrevna,
Shedding tears of sorrow and of bitterness.

Then her husband, Stepán Paramónovich,
Called his two young brothers unto him.
When they came, the younger brothers bowed
    respectfully,
And the following questions they addressed to him:
"Do thou tell us please, oh brother dear,
What grave thing has happened—what befallen thee?
Why didst ask us to come here in the dark of night—
In the dark of night, and the freezing cold?"

"I must tell you, kind-hearted brothers mine,
That a very great misfortune has befallen me.
Kiribéyevich, the evil bodyguard,
Has defiled the honor of our family.
'Tis the kind of outrage that the soul won't bear;
Nor will manly hearts suffer such things silently.
On the morrow, there will be fisticuffs
On Moskvá-Reká, for the Tsar to view.
I will challenge him then—the young bodyguard;
To the death I'll fight him—till my strength is spent.
If he vanquishes me, ye must challenge him,
For the sake of holy mother-truth.
Be ye not afraid, kind-hearted brothers mine!
Ye are younger than I, and more vigorous;
Ye have gathered less sins on your soul than I,
So to you the Lord may be merciful."

Then his brethren twain thus did answer him:
"Whither bloweth the wind in the sky above,

Thither hurry the clouds in obedience.
When the gray eagle screams, calling all to come
To the blood-soaked, narrow valley of the battlefield
For a feast, ready-spread, on the flesh of the dead,
Then the eaglets take wing to join him there.
Thou'rt the eldest son, and our second sire.
Do as thou desirest and thinkest good;
And thy trust, oh dearest brother, we'll not betray."

Ai, my hearties, sing out! But keep your zithers tuned!
Ai, my hearties, drink up! But do your duty, too!
Ye will pleasure the good Romodánovsky
And his lady, the fair-faced boyárynya.

III

Over mighty Moscow of the golden domes,
O'er the Kremlin's white stone walls and battlements,
From the forests afar, from the blue-ridged hills,
Touching timbered rooftops lightly, dartingly,
Sending clouds of gray quickly scattering,
The vermilion dawn doth reveal herself.
With her golden tresses flung back carelessly,
In the fine and powdery snowdrifts she washes herself.
Like a pretty maid at her looking glass,
She doth smile at the cloudless and perfect sky.

To what purpose, O vermilion dawn, has thou waked
this day?
What new joy attends on thee, that thou yearn'st to
play?

All the burly lads, Moscow's fighting men,

Have assembled in a throng on the frozen stream
Of Moskvá-Reká, for the fisticuffs—
To disport and amuse themselves, this holiday.
And the Tsar has come with his retinue—
With the bodyguards and boyars around him.
He has bade them lay out a silver chain before him;
Of the purest gold all the links are soldered.
Now a circle of some sixty yards has been chained off,
Where two fighters who are willing can trade fisticuffs.
At the order of Tsar Iván Vasíl'yevich,
The call is called out ringingly:
"Oh where are ye, stout-hearted fighting men?
Ye must pleasure the Tsar, our own father dear.
Come and take your place in the battle ring.
He that wins the bout, him the Tsar will reward.
He that loses out, let him look to the Lord!"

Kiribéyevich, the bold, now presents himself;
Bows low, wordless, in the Tsar's direction,
Throws off his velvet cloak from his mighty shoulders,
Props his good right hand against his hip, just so.
With his left hand he sets his scarlet cap in place,
Then awaits the man who'll dare contend with him.
Thrice the ringing call is called aloud.
Of the fighting men, not one stirs himself:
All stand still, doing nought but to nudge each other.

In the cleared space the Tsar's man struts pridefully,
As he mocks the cowardly fighters, and ridicules them.
"Why so quiet? I'll wager ye've thought twice by now!
Very well. Since today is a holiday,

I will spare my victim, to repent himself—
Just to pleasure the Tsar, our own father dear."

But a path through the throng opened suddenly,
And then out strode Stepán Paramónovich,
The young trading man, and bold fighting man,
With the family name of Kaláshnikov.
He saluted first the Tsar, the Awesome One,
Next, the silvery Kremlin and the holy shrines;
Lastly, all the Russian people gathered there.
His eyes blazed in his head like the falcon's eyes,
Staring fixedly at the bodyguard.
Now he takes his place straight across from him:
He draws on the leather gauntlets with care and
    patience;
His sinewy shoulders he doth flex and straighten;
Then his curly beard he strokes, deliberating.

Kiribéyevich thus accosted him:
"Do thou tell me now, valiant fighting man,
What thy family name and lineage is,
And the Christian name that thou goest by,
So they'll know for whom to sing Requiem Mass,
And so I may know whom to boast about."

Then Stepán, son of Páramon, answered him:
"Why, the name I bear is Stepán Kaláshnikov.
I was born the son of an honorable sire.
My life I've led according to Christian law:
I have never soiled another's wife,
Nor played highwayman in the dark of night,
Neither hidden myself from the heavens' light.

And the thing thou saidst was indeed most truthful:
For a funeral dirge will be sung for one of us
On the morrow, no later than the midday hour.
Likewise, one of us will be boasting, too,
As he revels with bold-hearted friends of his.
'Twas not just to chaff, just to make folk laugh,
That I challenged thee today, thou low infidel.
I challenge thee to mortal strife, for thy very life."

When he heard these words, Kiribéyevich
Turned all white of face, like the autumn snow;
O'er his impudent eyes came a cloudiness;
'Twixt his shoulder blades ran a sudden chill;
And his words froze in place on his parted lips.

In silence, both men retreat a pace:
Now the time has come for the bloody bout.

With a wide, looping swing, Kiribéyevich
Struck the opening blow at young Kaláshnikov.
On the trading man's chest did the blow strike home,
With such force that his ribs nearly cracked from it;
And it staggered Stepán Paramónovich.
'Round his powerful neck did hang a copper crucifix,
And within it were relics from Kiev town.
With the blow it bent, and did cut the flesh:
From beneath it, like the dew, blood ran trickling
    down.
Then Stepán Paramónovich told himself:
"What is destined to be, must needs come to pass.
I will fight for justice to the bitter end!"
With a new-found skill he did set himself,

Summoned up his every bit of strength,
And then, putting his whole shoulder behind the blow,
Struck his foe in the head, in the fatal spot.

And the youthful man-at-arms uttered one low moan,
Staggered briefly, and then collapsed in death.

At full length he fell, on the cold, cold snow—
On the cold, cold snow, like a sapling pine—
Like a sapling pine in the thick, damp woods,
When its resinous taproots are cut beneath it.
When he saw this thing, Tsar Iván Vasíl'yevich
Waxed most wroth and wrathful, and did stomp the
    earth.
Then he knit his brows most somberly,
And commanded the valorous merchant be seized
And then brought to him for an audience.

Quoth the Awesome Tsar of the Orthodox:
"Do thou tell me, in conscience and truthfully:
Was it knowingly, or unknowingly,
That thou didst to death my good servitor and true,
And my worthiest man-at-arms, Kiribéyevich?"

"I will tell thee true, Tsar of the Orthodox:
Of my own free will did I strike him dead.
But the cause thereof I'll not tell to thee:
I will tell it only to God Himself.
Do thou sentence me to death: bid my guilty head
Be transported to the chopping block.
But withhold not from my little ones,
And withhold not from my widow so young,
And my brethren twain, thy great clemency."

" 'Tis most fortunate, thou stalwart lad,
Valiant fighting man of the merchant class,
That thou gav'st reply as thy conscience bade.
To thy young, widowed wife and thy orphaned ones
I shall grant a sum from my treasury.
For thy brothers, I rule, from this very day,
That throughout all the far-flung realms of Muscovy,
They may trade sans tribute or customs fees.
But thyself must go, my sturdy lad,
To the towering execution dock,
And there lay down thy turbulent and restless head.
I will have an ax sharply whetted and honed,
Have the headsman don the best to be found,
And the Kremlin bell made to peal, resound,
To make known to all Moscow's inhabitants
That thou, too, didst not lack for my great clemency."

In the central square a throng has assembled, now;
And the bell is pealing, tolling dolefully,
As the evil tidings it tells far and wide.
On the towering execution dock,
In a scarlet shirt adorned with buttons bright,
With a ponderous ax whetted razor-keen,
Doth the headsman strut, full of cheerfulness.
Now he briskly rubs his hands together,
As he bides his time and waits for the fighter bold.

But the valiant one, the young merchant's son,
Doth yet bid farewell unto his brothers dear.

"Pay heed, ye brothers mine, friends and kinsmen
      both!
Come embrace me now for a parting kiss,
As we bid farewell, ne'er to meet again.
Please remember me to dear Alyóna Dmítrevna.
Do ye tell her to temper her grief for me,
And not to speak of their father's fate to the little ones.
Please remember me to our father's household;
And remember me to all our comrades, too.
Ye yourselves say prayers in the holy church
For a sin-laden soul—for your brother's soul!"

So they punished the merchant Kaláshnikov
With a frightful death, and infamous;
And his hapless head, that such grief had known,
Rolled in bloody welter on the chopping block.

On the Moscow's far bank did they bury him,
In open country where three roadways meet
Called the Túla, Ryazán, and Vladímir roads.
And a mound of cold, damp earth they heaped over
      him;
And a maple cross they did set in it.
Now the boisterous winds, sporting riotously,
Dance and howl o'er his lonely and nameless grave.
And the good folk often chance to pass that way:
When an old man passes by, he doth cross himself;
When a brave youth goes by, he doth strut a bit;
And when a maid goes by, she grieves silently.
But when the minstrels go by, then a song rings out.

Bold lads in whom green youth is springing,
Ye who strum with your singing,
Ye whose voices are ringing!
Your song began bravely—now finish it bravely, too!
Render to each one the praise that to him is due.
To the goodly Romodánovsky—glory!
To his beauteous boyárynya—glory!
And to all the Christian people everywhere—glory!

(1837)

FROM The Novice

I

Not very many years ago,
At that point where two rushing streams,
The Arágva and the Kúra, come
Together, in a close embrace
Like two young sisters, there once stood
A monastery. Even now,
From the far side of the mountain's crest,
The traveler can see the towers,
The ruined columns of the gates,
And the vaulted dome. But in the church
Beneath, the censer's fragrant smoke
No longer smolders; and at night
One can no longer hear the chant
Of holy monks, praying for us.
Today, one aged, gray-haired man,
The half-live guardian of the ruins,
Forgotten by all living folk
And death as well, brushes the dust
From tombstones whose inscriptions tell
Tales of past glory; and of how,
Finding his crown too burdensome,
A certain king, in a certain year,
Gave o'er his tribe to Russian rule.

And the blessings of the Lord were brought
To Georgia. Since then, in the shade
Of her green gardens, she has flowered—
Safe from her enemies, behind
A hedge of friendly bayonets.

XIII

Holding a pitcher on her head,
A Georgian girl was coming down
A narrow pathway toward the stream.
From time to time, her foot would slip
Between two rocks, and she would smile
At her misstep. Her clothes were plain,
And she moved lightly, the long folds
Of her *chadrá* * thrown back across
Her shoulders. Scorching summer heat
Had burned her lovely face and throat
A golden brown, and sultriness
Suffused her cheeks and her red lips.
Her black eyes were so deep, so full
Of love's dark lore, that my inflamed
Thoughts were distracted. All I can
Remember is the ringing sound
Made by the pitcher on the rocks
As water flowed into it: this
And a slight rustle—nothing more.

When I recovered, and the blood
Flowed freely from my heart again,

---

* A *chadra* is a kind of long veil worn by native women in the Caucasus.

She was already far away,
Moving more slowly, but with grace
And harmony beneath her load,
Like an aspen tree, queen of the fields!
A short way off, in the cool mist,
Seeming to grow upon the cliff,
Were two small huts set side by side.
Above the low, flat roof of one
A column of blue smoke rose up.
I see, as if it were right now,
The door being opened carefully
And, after her, closing again.

I know that you don't understand
My heartache—my unhappiness;
And I'd be sorry if you could.
The memories of those moments still
Live in me. Let them die with me.

(1839)

LATER LYRICS AND OTHER SHORT POEMS

(1837–1841)

The Prisoner

Open up this dreary prison!
Let me see the day outside.
Let me have a black-eyed maiden,
And a black-maned horse to ride.
First I'll kiss my dark-eyed beauty
Long and tenderly; then, leaping
On my horse with jet-black mane,
I'll whirl away across the plain.

High the prison's narrow window,
Stout the door, and bolted tight;
Far away, in her high tower,
Waits the maiden through the night.
My faithful steed, in some green meadow,
Happily, without his bridle,
Romps and plays, alone and free,
His tail aflutter in the breeze.

I'm alone: none can console me.
The naked walls crowd close about;
The ikon lamp is burning dimly—
Slowly, surely flickering out.

Only one sound breaks the stillness:
Through the night hours, as I listen
Ceaselessly, I hear with dread
The tight-lipped sentry's measured tread.

(1837)

Farewell, Unwashed Russia!

Farewell forever, unwashed Russia!
O land of slaves, and masters cruel!
And you, blue-uniformed * oppressors!
And you, meek nation whom they rule!

Beyond the Caucasus' high ridges,
I may be safe from your viziers †—
From their all-seeing eyes quite hidden,
And far from their all-hearing ears.

(1837)

Clouds

Clouds in the heavens, eternally wandering!
Across the blue steppe like a long string of pearls, you go

---

* First stanza, line three: the original has only ". . . (light) blue uniforms"; but the unequivocal reference, as understood by Lermontov's contemporaries, was to the political police ("gendarmes") of Nicholas I.

† Second stanza, line two: 'viziers' is *not* a forced rhyme, but a synonym for the term 'pashas'—commonly applied to high officials in the political police.

Quickly, as though you were exiled, as I am now,
From the dear North to the far-distant southern lands.

What is it that drives you? A verdict of Destiny?
Envy felt secretly? Evil done openly?
Or are you burdened by crimes of your own doing?
Or by the venomous slander of friends of yours?

No, you were weary of fields where no harvest grew . . .
Strangers to passion, and strangers to suffering,
Eternally cold and eternally free, you roam:
You have no homeland, exile there is none for you.

(1840)

A Soldier's Testament

Just for a moment, friend, I'd like
To be alone with you.
From what I hear, my earthly life
Is pretty nearly through.
You'll soon be going home; and so
I thought . . . But what's the use? I know—
To put it to you bluntly—
Nobody cares about me.

But if somebody should ask you—
Whoever it might be—
Tell them a bullet got me through
The chest. Tell them for me
That I died honorably for the Tsar;

How blundering our doctors are;
And that I send my homage
And greetings to our homeland.

I don't think there's much chance you'll find
My mother and my dad
Alive— Besides, I wouldn't like
To have them take it hard.
But if they are alive, you might
Tell them I'm too lazy to write;
That the regiment's moved forward,
And I won't get a furlough.

There was a girl, as you'll recall . . .
How very long ago
We parted! She won't ask at all
About me. Even so,
Tell her the whole thing from the start:
Don't spare her cold and empty heart.
And if she cries—well, let her!
To her, it doesn't matter.

(1840)

From Sophie Karamzina's Album

Note: *Sophia Karamzina—oldest daughter of
Nicholas Karamzin (1766–1826), historian and leader
of the Sentimentalist school of Russian fiction, who
largely reformed literary Russian: she presided with
wit and graciousness over a salon whose habitués*

included Pushkin, Gogol, Zhukovsky, et al. Smir-
nova—Alexandra Smirnova-Rosset, a member of the
same circle. "Sashka"—Alexander Karamzin, So-
phia's brother. "Ishka"—Ivan Myatlev, author of
a comic verse novel in the "macaronic" (multi-
lingual) manner, The Sensations and Observations
of Madame Fat Tail Abroad, dans /sic/ l'étranger.
—Ed.

When I was young and knew no better
(In days which now are gone for good)
I used to love wild, stormy weather,
And stormy passions in my blood.

But soon the secret of their formless
Beauty revealed itself to me:
I found their savage accents boresome—
All deafening noise, no harmony.

Now more and more, with each year's turning,
As my desires grow more humdrum,
I love fine weather in the morning,
And quiet talk when evening comes.

I love your witty paradoxes—
Your ha, ha, ha and hee, hee, hee;
Smirnova's capers, Sasha's farces,
And Ishka's wacky poetry.

(1841)

The Captive Knight

Silent I sit in this gaol, by the window;
Through it I see the blue sky far above me:
There, in the heavens, the birds fly so freely!
Watching them, I am ashamed and tormented.

My tongue has not sinned by reciting a prayer;
Nor have I chanted the praise of my loved one:
The battles of old days are all I remember—
These, and my broadsword, and armor of iron.

Now I am held in a suit of stone armor;
A helmet of stone presses down on my forehead.
My shield has been charmed against arrow and swordthrust;
My charger runs free, with no rider to rein him.

My charger, unfailing, is Time—ever-fleeting;
The grating that bars the high casement—my visor;
The prison's high walls are my suit of stone armor;
The stout iron door is my shield of forged iron.

Hurry on faster, O Time, in thy coursing!
Stifled am I in this new suit of armor!
Death, when we get there, will hold up my stirrup;
I shall dismount, and at last raise my visor.

(1840)

Native Land

I love my native land, but with a strange devotion—
A love that reason cannot dominate.

Not glory, bought with blood of soldiers,
Nor deep serenity, expressing a proud faith,
Nor yet the hallowed tales of times now dim and shadowed,
Can quicken, in myself, such musings as bring gladness.

The things I love (I know not why) are these:
The cold, bleak silence of her empty steppe lands;
The swaying motion of her boundless forests;
Her overflowing rivers, so resembling seas. . . .
I love to race along back roads in a telega
Through the darkness of the night, and as I look around,
To see on either hand, like promises of shelter,
The tiny, flickering lights of mournful little towns.

I love the smoke from burned-off stubble;
Wagon-trains on the steppe at night;
On rising ground, in yellow cornfields,
Twin birch trees, dazzlingly white.
With a pleasure quite unknown to many,
I note the granary's pregnant line;
The thatched roof of the peasant shanty;
Its shutters, with their carved design.

And on cool evenings, when there's dancing,
I'll stay up half the night to watch,
And hear the whistling and stamping,
And the hum of drunken peasants' talk.

(1841)

The Rock Ledge

Through the night, a golden cloud lay sleeping
On the breast of a gigantic rock ledge.
In the morning, early, off she hurried;
Through the azure, carefree, she went playing.

But a trace of moisture was still clinging
To the wrinkled rock ledge. Old and lonely,
He stood there as though in sad reflection—
In the empty spaces softly weeping.

(1841)

Tamara *

In the deep mountain gorge of Daryálsky,
Where the Térek flows, burrowing through gloom,
Stood an ancient stone tower, even blacker
Than the black cliff against which it loomed.

In that tower, so high and so narrow,
The Tsarítsa Tamara once dwelled:
She was fair as an angel from Heaven,
And as evil as something from Hell.

From the tower, through the late evening darkness,
Shone a yellowish light; and its glare

---

* The poem is based on an old Georgian legend. The Terek is a river
in the Caucasus region which at one point flows through the Daryálsky
Canyon or Gorge (*Daryálskoe Ushchéle*).

Promised shelter and warmth to the traveler
Who would tarry to spend the night there.

He would hear, then, the voice of Tamara:
Of passion it sang, and desire;
It was filled with a strange, potent magic,
And an incomprehensible power.

With the sound of her voice, the enchantress
Would entice merchant, shepherd, or knight
To the tower—to be met at the entrance
By a eunuch as black as the night;

While above Queen Tamara, reclining
On her bed in her finest array,
With two goblets of wine set beside her,
Awaited her guest—and her prey.

Then hot hands would entwine with each other,
As lips upon lips were glued fast;
And strange, savage cries would re-echo
Until long after midnight was past.

It was though, in that old, empty castle,
Fifty lusty young couples, just wed,
Had convened for a night wedding party—
Or a riotous feast for the dead.

But as soon as the first light of daybreak
Tinged the mountains around it, the tower
Would be plunged into silence; and darkness
Would instantly reign there once more.

There would come to that deep, narrow canyon
A stillness like that of the grave,

With only the sound of the current,
As gray wave followed fast on gray wave,

And, splashing, made haste to take with it
A corpse that had started to drift
Down the stream; while above, in a window,
Something flashed, and a voice said, "Forgive!"

But her words of farewell were as tender,
And the sound of her voice was as sweet,
As a promise of loving caresses,
Or of rapture, as when lovers meet.

(1841)

The Oak Leaf

An oak leaf was torn by the wind from the branch he had
grown on;
And driven by merciless storms, to the steppe he went
flying;
The heat and the cold and his grief made him withered
and faded;
And finally he came to the edge of a sea in the Southland.

And there, on the edge of the sea, stood a pretty young
plane tree.
The wind softly stroked her green leaves as it whispered
and murmured;
And on her green branches sat tropical birds, who were
swaying
And singing her songs of the glory of Princess Marina.

The traveler approached to the trunk of the beautiful
    plane tree;
And, yearning and sighing, he begged her to give him
    some shelter.
And thus he began: "I'm a poor little leaf from an oak tree.
I fell off too soon and grew up in a harsh kind of country.

"Alone, all these years, through the world I've been
    aimlessly drifting;
Deprived of green shade, sleep, and peace, I am withered
    and faded.
Won't you please give me shelter among your own leaves
    of bright emerald?
I'll tell you all kinds of fine tales full of wisdom and
    marvels!"

"And what's that to me?" the young plane tree then
    scornfully answered.
"You're dusty and brown and unworthy of my sons' green
    freshness.
You've seen many things . . . Well, so what do I want
    with your stories?
The tropical birds long ago tired my ears with their singing.

"Get moving, you wanderer! Be on your way! I don't know
    you!
The sun is my lover: for him my leaves flourish and glitter.
And here in this part of the sky I have spread out my
    branches;
And here my deep roots are washed clean by the cold
    ocean water."

(1841)

The Prophet

> Note: *This is Lermentov's rejoinder to Pushkin's poem with the same title (1826), which exalted the role of the poet as prophet.*—ED.

Since that day when the Lord on high
Endowed me with a prophet's knowledge,
I've read in every human eye
A chronicle of vice and folly.

Love I proclaimed; and I began
To teach the Truth—simply and purely:
My neighbors rose up as one man
And threw stones at me in their fury.

I sprinkled ashes on my head
And ran off, homeless, to the wildwood;
Now, like the little birds, I feed
On those things that the Lord provideth.

In keeping with His covenant,
Beasts of the wilderness obey me;
Stars, dancing in the firmament
For joy, all hearken to my sayings.

But when I quickly make my way
Through the crowds and clamor of the city,
The old men point at me and say
With a sneering smile, "Look at him, children!

"There's an example for you! He
Was proud, and wouldn't do as we did.

The fool tried to make us believe
That God would speak to us as he did.

"Take a good look! Just see how grim
And glum he is—how thin and haggard!
Just look: he's poor, his clothes are ragged,
And everyone despises him!"

(1841)

I Walk Alone Along the Highway

I walk alone at night along the highway;
Through the haze glitters the road's rough spar.
The night is still; the silent spaces hearken
To God; a star sends signals to a star.

Marvelous and solemn are the heavens!
The earth is sleeping in a pale blue light.
Then why am I so troubled and so heartsick?
Do I still hope? Or do I feel regret?

But I ask nothing that this life can offer;
About the past I've no regrets at all.
Peace and freedom—these are what I long for:
I'd like just to forget myself, and fall

Into a sleep. Yet not the grave's cold numbness . . .
I'd like a sleep eternal that would leave,
Within myself, the strength of life still slumbering,
So I might breathe, and my breast gently heave;

So that both day and night, ever so sweetly,
A tender voice would sing to me of love;
And where I lay, a great oak, ever greening,
With rustling leaves would bend down from above.

(1841)

Princess Ligovskaya

Note: *Lermontov's work on this novel, begun in 1836, was broken off by his arrest early in 1837. Portions of Ms. are written in the hand of Lermontov's friend, S. A. Raevsky. This, plus the fact that the poet, in a letter to Raevsky, mentions "the novel we began," suggests a possible collaboration. However, Lermontov often dictated works-in-progress to friends; and Raevsky is reported to have told at least one memoirist that he merely served as amanueniss in the case of* Ligovskaya. *Accordingly, the concensus of scholarly opinion is that the novel was not a product of collaboration.* —ED.

Chapter One

> *Make way! Make way! the shout rang out.*[1]
> —PUSHKIN

At four o'clock on the afternoon of December 21, 1833, the usual throng of people was moving along Voznesenskaya Street in St. Petersburg. Among them was a young government clerk. Please take note of the day and the hour; because on that day and at that hour there occurred an event leading to many different adventures involving all those characters, male and female, whose story I have promised to transmit to posterity—provided posterity takes to reading novels.

[1] A line from *Eugene Onegin* (Chapter One, Stanza XVI) emphasizing the link between *Princess Ligovskaya* and Pushkin's masterpiece.

As I said, a young government clerk was walking along Voznesenskaya Street. He was on his way home from the office, worn out by his monotonous work and daydreaming of a bonus and a tasty dinner (for all government clerks have their dreams!). He wore a cap of no very definite shape, and a blue overcoat of wadded material with an old beaver collar. His features were difficult to make out—the reasons for this being the bill of his cap, the collar of his coat, and the semidarkness. Apparently he was not hurrying home, but was enjoying the fresh air of the frosty evening, which suffused the rooftops with a pinkish glow in the winter darkness—that, and the alluring glitter of the stores and confectioners' shops. From time to time, having raised his eyes heavenward in truly poetic rapture, he would collide with a pink bonnet, and then apologize in great embarrassment. The perfidious pink bonnet would fly into a rage. Then she would ogle him under the bill of his cap; and having gone on a few steps, she would stop and turn around as though expecting a second apology. But in vain! The young clerk was completely unaware of her game.

But even more frequently he would stop to peer into the show-window of a store or confectioner's shop, glittering with marvelous lights and splendid gilt. He would stare long, intently, and covetously at the various articles. Then, coming back to himself, with a deep sigh and a stoic resolve he would continue on his way.

His worst tormentors, though, were the hackney drivers. He hated the hackney drivers. "Where to, sir? Shall I

drive you? Let me drive you." It was the torture of
Tantalus. And from the very depths of his soul he hated
the hackney drivers.

He had walked down the slope from Voznesensky Bridge
and was about to turn right along the canal, when suddenly he heard a shout: "Look out there! Make way!" A
bay trotting horse was rushing straight at him. Behind
the driver he glimpsed the white plume of an officer's
shako and the collar of a gray overcoat flapping in the
wind. He had scarcely looked up when one of the carriage
shafts was against his chest and his face was immersed in
the steam from the horse's nostrils. Automatically, he
grasped the carriage shaft. At the same moment a powerful
lunge of the horse threw him several feet to one side and
onto the sidewalk.

"He ran him down! He ran him down!" the onlookers
shouted. And the hackney drivers took out in pursuit of
the lawbreaker. But the white plume remained only briefly
in view, and then vanished.

When the clerk recovered his senses, he felt no pain
anywhere; but his knees were still trembling from fright.
He stood up, leaned on the guard rail along the canal,
and tried to clear his head. His heart was full of bitterness.
And from that moment, all the hatred his soul could
muster was transferred from hackney drivers to bay trotters
and white plumes.

Meantime, the white plume and the bay trotter had
dashed along the canal, turned into Nevsky Prospect, from
there to Karavannaya Street, thence over the Simionovsky

Bridge, and then turned right into the Fontanka, where they drew up at an elegant porte cochere before a glass door with gleaming fixtures of brass.

"Well, sir," said the driver, a broad-shouldered peasant with a bushy read beard, "I guess Vaska showed his mettle back there!"

It should be noted that coachmen always call their favorite horse "Vaska," against the wishes of the owners, who gave them such sonorous names as "Achilles" and "Hector." For the coachman, the horse will never be "Achilles" or "Hector," but always "Vaska."

The officer got out, patted the steaming horse on his arched neck, gave him a grateful smile, and went up the highly polished steps. He did not so much as mention the clerk he had run down.

Now, as he takes off his overcoat, sprinkled with snow, and goes into his study, we are free to follow him and describe his appearance, which unfortunately was not at all attractive. He was short, broad in the shoulders, and in general rather ungainly. He seemed to have a powerful constitution, incapable of sensitivity or irritation. His gait was rather cautious for a cavalryman. His gestures were abrupt, although they sometimes displayed that indolence and indifference which are now modish and in the spirit of the times (if this is not a pleonasm). But the man's real nature frequently broke through this cold exterior. It was evident that he did not follow the general fashion, but kept his thoughts and feelings tightly closed within himself—either from mistrustfulness or from pride. His voice was sometimes deep, sometimes sharp, depending upon the influence of the moment. When he wanted to say something pleasant, he would begin to stammer, and then break off abruptly with an acid witticism in order to hide his own embarrassment. And in society it was said that his tongue was malicious and dangerous; because society cannot tolerate anything powerful and upsetting—anything which might reveal character and strength of will. Society demands French vaudevilles and Russian deference to foreign opinion.

His face was swarthy, with irregular features, but very expressive. It would have been very interesting to Lavater [2] and his followers, who would have found in it deep traces of the past and marvelous promise for the future. But most people merely said that in his smile, and in his strangely glittering eyes, there was something indefinable.

By way of completing this portrait I will tell you that his name was Grigory Aleksandrovich Pechorin (or, among intimates, simply "George" in the French manner); that he was twenty-three years old; and that his parents had three thousand serfs in the provinces of Saratov, Voronezh, and Kaluga. (I add this last bit of information in order to embellish his appearance somewhat in the eyes of morally strict readers.)

I must apologize. I forgot to say that George was an only son, not counting his sister, a girl of sixteen who was really quite pretty. According to her mama (her papa was no longer alive) she had no need of a dowry and

2 Johann Kaspar Lavater (1741–1801), Swiss poet, philosopher, and theologian. His writings on the art of "physiognomy" (not phrenology, but rather the interpretation of the play of facial expression) attracted the admiring attention of a whole school of "Lavaterians," including Goethe.

could reach a high place in society with the help of God, her pretty face, and a brilliant upbringing.

Once in his study, Grigory Aleksandrovich sank into a big armchair. A servant came in and reported that, as he put it, milady had deigned to dine out with friends, and the master's sister had deigned to have her dinner already. "I shall not dine," came the answer. "I have lunched." Then another servant entered—a small boy of thirteen in a red Cossack jacket: sharp-eyed, pale of complexion, and to all appearances a rogue. Without saying a word, he handed over a visiting card. Pechorin perfunctorily tossed the card on his writing desk, and asked who had brought it.

"A young lady and her husband were here just now," Fedka answered. "They told me to give the card to Tatyana Petrovna." (This was the name of Pechorin's mother.)

"Then why did you bring it to me?"

"I thought it didn't make any difference. I thought perhaps you would like to read it."

"In other words, you would like to know what is written on it."

"Yes, sir. The lady and gentleman were never here before."

"I have spoiled you," Pechorin said sternly. "Here. Take my pipe and fill it."

It was plain to see that the visiting card had aroused his curiosity. Yet for a long time he could not bring himself to change his comfortable position in the big armchair and reach over to the writing desk. Moreover, there was no candlelight in the room. It was illuminated by the reddish glow from the fireplace; and he was reluctant to have the candles brought in and thereby spoil the bewitching effect of the firelight.

But his curiosity prevailed. He arose, picked up the calling card, and with a vague feeling of apprehension, held it close to the fireplace screen. On it, in Gothic letters, was inscribed: *Prince Stepan Stepanych Ligovskoy, and Princess Ligovskaya.*

Pechorin started. His face turned pale and his eyes flashed. The card fell into the fireplace.

For a few minutes he paced back and forth in the room, making strange gestures with one hand, and uttering various exclamations, sometimes smiling, at other times frowning. At length he stopped, seized the tongs, and rushed to retrieve the card from the fire. But in vain. Half of it was already ashes. On the other half, which was crumpled and scorched, he could scarcely make out the words *Stepan Step* . . . Pechorin placed the scorched fragment on his desk, sat down in his armchair, and covered his face with his hands. It is precisely for this reason that I cannot tell you anything at all about his thoughts, although I am very good at reading in people's faces what is happening in their souls.

He had been sitting there for a quarter of an hour when suddenly he heard a kind of rustling sound, as of a dress, or a sheet of paper, or light footsteps. Although he did not believe in apparitions, he started, raising his head quickly. In the semidarkness he saw before him something white and, as it seemed, ethereal. For a moment he did not know what to make of it, so far had his thoughts strayed—if not from this world, then at least from that room.

"Who is it?" he asked.

"Me!" came the reply, in an affected contralto, followed by a clear-ringing feminine laugh.

"Varenka! What a prankster you are!"

"You were asleep! How terribly amusing."

"I wish I were asleep—then things would be more peaceful."

"Shame on you! That's why it's always so boring for us girls at parties and balls. You men are always looking for tranquility. What delightful young fellows!"

"And may I be permitted to inquire," said George, yawning, "why we are obliged to entertain you?"

"Because we are women."

"Congratulations! But the fact is that *we* are not bored without *you*."

"I ought to know! But what are we supposed to talk about among ourselves?"

"Oh, the fashions, the news. Isn't that enough? Then tell each other your secrets."

"What secrets? I don't have any secrets . . . All young men are so unbearable. . . ."

"Most of them are not used to feminine society."

"Then let them get used to it! They don't even want to try!"

George rose to his feet solemnly, and bowed with a mocking smile. "Varvara Aleksandrovna, I can see that you are making great strides toward the cult of enlightenment."

Varenka blushed, and her red lips formed into a pout. But her brother, with the utmost calm, merely sat down again in his armchair. Meantime, the candles were brought in. Now, while Varenka is sulking and drumming on the window with her fingertips, I shall describe for you the room we are in.

It was a combination study and living room, and was connected by a corridor to the other part of the house. The walls were papered in French blue. The gleaming oak doors with their fashionable knobs, and the oak window frames, showed that the owner was a respectable and orderly person. The window drapes were of the Chinese variety. In the evening, or when the sun shone directly into the windows, the crimson blinds were lowered. The contrast with the colors in the room was rather sharp; but it indicated a certain fondness for the strange and unusual. Opposite the window was a writing desk covered with a litter of sketches, paper, books, various inkstands, and fashionable bric-a-brac. On one side stood a high trellis covered with an impenetrable tangle of green ivy. On the other was the armchair in which George was now sitting. A large rug with varicolored arabesque designs was on the floor beneath it. Another Persian rug covered the wall opposite the window. On it were hung some pistols, two Turkish rifles, and some Circassian sabers and knives—gifts from fellow officers who had been beyond the Balkans at one time or another. Three alabaster busts—of Paganini, Ivanov,[3] and Rossini—stood on the marble mantelpiece.

[3] Nikolay Kuzmich Ivanov (1810–80), a celebrated Russian singer.

The other walls were bare. Long divans upholstered in crimson damask extended along them and around the room. One single picture caught the eye. It was a portrait of an unidentified masculine face, painted by an obscure Russian artist unaware of his own genius, which no one had bothered to point out to him. The picture was a piece of fantasy, profound and gloomy. The face was rendered directly, without any artificial distortions or effects. The light fell from above. The clothing had been painted crudely, vaguely, and carelessly, as though the artist had concentrated all of his attention upon the eyes and the smile. The head was larger than life-size, and the hair fell evenly along both sides of the forehead, which was very prominent and seemed to have something extraordinary in its structure. The eyes, which looked straight ahead, shone with that strange glitter which eyes sometimes have when glimpsed through the slits of a black mask. Their probing and reproachful look seemed to follow one into every corner of the room; and the smile on the thin, tight lips was more contemptuous than mocking. Each time George looked at the face he saw a new expression in it. It had become his companion in moments of solitude and day-dreaming. And he, as an admirer of Byron, called it a portrait of Lara. Those friends to whom he showed it, said merely that it was a rather decent picture.

While I was describing the study, Varenka gradually approached the desk, then came closer to her brother and sat down in a chair opposite him. Her gray-blue eyes showed no trace of her momentary anger; but she was at a loss how to renew the conversation. Then she noticed the half-burned calling card.

"What's this? '*Stepan Step* . . .' Why, Prince Ligovskoy must have come to call on us! How I should like to see Verochka! To think that she's married now . . . she was so good . . . I heard yesterday that they had come here from Moscow . . . But who burned this card? It should have been taken to Mama."

"I would seem to be the guilty party," George said, "I used it to light my pipe."

"That's just fine! I only wish Verochka knew . . . she would be so pleased! It is plain to see, sir, that you have a fickle heart! Well, I'll tell her—I certainly will! On second thought, no. It probably wouldn't make any difference to her now. After all, she *is* married."

"You are very judicious for your years," her brother said, and then yawned, not knowing what to add.

"For my years! Am I supposed to be a child? Mama says a girl of seventeen is as intelligent as a man of twenty-five."

"You are very wise to listen to your mother."

This remark, which might have been taken for praise, turned out to be a bit of sarcasm, so that the harmony between them was again disturbed, and they both fell silent.

The servant boy entered, bringing a note. It was an invitation to a ball being given by Baron R_____.

"What a bore!" George exclaimed. "We'll have to go."

"Mademoiselle Negouroff [4] will be there," Varenka replied ironically. "She was asking about you yesterday. What beautiful eyes she has! Enchanting!"

"*Like glowing coals in a forge!*" [5]

"Come, now. You must admit she has marvelous eyes."

"When you hear someone's eyes praised, it means the rest isn't worth anything."

"You laugh! But you yourself aren't exactly indifferent to her."

"No doubt."

"I'm going to tell Verochka about that, too!"

"Not so long ago you were telling me that for her I— it doesn't matter!"

"Believe me, I speak Russian better than that. I wasn't reared in a convent! [6]

"Oh, by no means! Far from it!"

She blushed and left the room.

But I should explain to you that this was a bad day for the two of them. Usually they were very close; and George, especially, had the tenderest brotherly love for his sister.

Varenka's last allusion to Mademoiselle Negouroff (as we shall call her from now on) had put George into a mood of deep reflection. Finally an unexpected idea came to him from on high. He moved the inkstand closer, took

[4] The French spelling of Negurov, the girl's last name, which in its feminine form is Negurova, as it appears later.

[5] From an ode by Mikhail Vasil'yevich Lomonosov (1714–1765), poet and scientist; the "Russian Leonardo," of peasant origin.

[6] Varvara means specifically that she was not educated at a certain fashionable convent school where French was spoken to the virtual exclusion of Russian.

out a sheet of stationery, and began to write. As he wrote, a smile of self-satisfaction would frequently appear on his face, and his eyes would sparkle. In short, he was in very gay spirits, like a man who has thought of something extraordinary.

When he finished writing he put the letter into an envelope and addressed it: *Miss Elizaveta Lvovna* [7] *Negurova. Personal.* Then he rang for Fedka and told him to take it to the city post office, and to avoid being seen by any of the other servants. The little Mercury, proud of the great trust placed in him by his master, dashed off for the post office. Pechorin then ordered his sleigh to be made ready; and a half-hour later he left for the opera. On this trip, however, he didn't succeed in running down a single government clerk.

Chapter Two

They were giving the fourth performance of *Fenella.*[1] The narrow passageway leading to the ticket window was jammed with people. Pechorin, who did not yet have a ticket and was impatient, spoke to a theater employee who was selling programs. For fifteen rubles he got an orchestra seat in the second row on the left, and on the outside—

[7] In later references the young lady's "middle name" (patronymic, or "father's name") is given as 'Nikolavna' ("daughter of Nikolay") rather than 'Lvovna' ("daughter of Lev"), as here.

[1] "Fenella" (after the name of the heroine) was the popular appellation in Russia for *La Muette de Portici*, the opera by Daniel François Auber, with a libretto by Eugène Scribe.

a great advantage for those who want to spare their feet, and who are going to the Phoenix Restaurant for tea during intermission.

When Pechorin entered, they had not yet begun playing the overture, and some of the box seats were not yet occupied. In the dress circle, directly above him, was an empty box; and seated next to it were the Negurov family —father, mother, and daughter. The daughter would have been quite attractive except for the pallor, thinness, and lack of youthfulness in her face (a shortcoming almost general among the young ladies of St. Petersburg), which eclipsed the brilliance of her very large eyes and destroyed the harmony between her quite regular features and intelligent expression. She nodded to Pechorin rather affectionately, and smiled brightly.

Obviously, he told himself, my letter has not yet reached its addressee; and he directed his opera glass toward the other box seats. Among their occupants he recognized many people he had met at balls. To some of them he nodded, to others he didn't, depending upon whether they had recognized him. He did not take offense at society's indifference toward him, because he rated society at its real worth. He knew that it is easy to make oneself a topic of conversation. But he also knew that society does not take up the same person twice in succession: it requires ever new idols, new fashions, new romances. The veterans of celebrity, like all other veterans, are very sad specimens. In a small social circle where intelligent, varied conversation replaced dancing (not to mention those affairs called "routs"), where one could discuss anything and everything without fearing the censorship of one's aunts, and without encountering stern and unapproachable virgins—in such a circle he might have shone. He might even have been considered charming, because when intelligence and qualities of soul find outward expression, they lend life and mobility to one's features, so that their defects are forgotten. But there are very few such social circles in Russia, and even less of them in Petersburg—despite the fact that it is called a completely European city and the arbiter of good taste. (In passing I should like to add that good taste reigns only where one hears nothing excessive. But alas, my friends! How little you will hear in such places!)

When he went to a ball, Pechorin, with his unattractive appearance, would lose himself in the crowd of onlookers; and he would be either melancholy or overly malicious, because his self-esteem was suffering. Since he rarely danced, he could strike up a conversation only with the wallflowers; but these were the very ones with whom he never really formed an acquaintanceship. There had been a time when he devoted himself to satire. Standing off to one side from the couples dancing the mazurka, he would analyze them aloud; and his caustic comments would soon be repeated throughout the ballroom and the whole city. But once, during a mazurka, he chanced to overhear the talk between a tall, thin diplomat and a princess. The diplomat was plagiarizing all of Pechorin's own witty comments, and only a sense of decorum kept the princess from laughing uproariously. Pechorin recalled that three days before, when he had said the same things (and said them much better) to a nymph of the social set, she had merely shrugged her shoulders and had not even taken the trouble to understand him. From that time on he began to dance more and do less intelligent talking; and he even had the impression that people were beginning to accept him with great pleasure. In a word, he began to understand that *according to the basic laws of society, intelligence in a dancing partner is out of place.*

The orchestra struck up the overture. Every seat was occupied except for the box next to the Negurovs, which frequently attracted Pechorin's curious glances. He found the situation strange; and he would have liked very much to have a look at the people who had missed the overture to *Fenella.*

The curtain went up; and at the same moment there was the scraping of chairs being moved in the empty box seat. Pechorin looked up, but could see only a crimson beret and, resting negligently on the red velvet edge of the box, a divine, plumpish little white hand holding a divine lorgnette. He tried several times to observe the movements of the unknown lady, to see whether he could glimpse so much as her eyes or her cheek, but in vain. Once he leaned so far back that he could have seen her forehead and her eyes. But as though to spite him, a huge pair of opera glasses blocked out the entire upper part of her face. His neck was aching. He was infuriated, and vowed he would look no more at that damned box seat. When the first act was over, he got up and went with some friends to the Phoenix, trying to avoid even a chance look at the much-loathed box seat.

The Phoenix Restaurant is very remarkable by virtue

of its topographic location with respect to the stage doors of the Aleksandrinsky Theatre. O Phoenix! There was a time when ugly old carriages pulled by a pair of lame nags crowded up to the narrow doors of the theater, and young nymphs with coarse, government-issue [2] shawls thrown over their shoulders sprang onto the squeaky footboards, while a throng of mustachioed gallants armed with sparkling lorgnettes and even more sparkling glances, would crowd upon your steps! But those roaring days soon passed. And now, where black and white plumes used to wave, one sees tricorn hats without plumes decorously taking the air. A great example of the revolutions in man's fate!

Pechorin went into the Phoenix with an officer from the Preobrazhensky Regiment and another from the horse-drawn artillery. He ordered tea, and sat down at a table with them. The restaurant was crowded with a great variety of people. Sitting at the same table as Pechorin was a young man in a frock coat whose attire was not altogether distinguished. He was smoking his own home-made cigarettes, which made the waiters very curious. The young man was tall, blond, and astoundingly good-looking. His large, languid gray eyes, straight nose (like that of the Belvedere Apollo), the Greek oval of his face, and his beautiful, naturally curly hair, were enough to attract the attention of anyone. Only his lips, which were too thin and pale in contrast to the color in his cheeks, might have been found wanting. From the brass buttons on his coat, with the State Seal stamped upon them, one could tell

[2] "Government-issue" because the opera was an enterprise of the Imperial Government, which provided all such necessaries.

that he was a government clerk—like all frock-coated young men in St. Petersburg.

He was plunged deep in thought and seemed not to be listening to the talk of the officers, who were joking, laughing, and telling anecdotes as they washed down the smoke from their pipes with bad tea. Among other things, they began to talk about horses. One artillery officer was praising his trotter. A dispute arose. Apropos of this, Pechorin told how, on that same day, he had run down a young dandy on the Voznesensky Bridge and then escaped his pursuers. He described the clothes worn by the dandy in the crumpled cap, and his unfortunate position on the sidewalk. The others laughed.

When Pechorin had finished the young man in the frock coat arose and, as he was reaching for his hat on the table, knocked to the floor the tray with the teapot and teacups. His gesture had obviously been deliberate. All eyes were turned upon him. But Pechorin's look was sharper and more questioning than the others. The stranger's face was flushed. He remained immobile and did not apologize. The silence lasted a full minute. A little circle of people formed, and everybody expected a scandal. But Pechorin sat down again and called loudly to the waiter: "How much is the tea service worth?"

A figure double its value was named.

"This clerk was clumsy enough to break it," George went on coldly. "Here is the money for it." And he added: "Tell him he is free to leave, now."

The waiter respectfully informed the clerk, in front of everyone, that he had been fully compensated—and then asked for a tip! But the latter, without saying a word, left the restaurant. There was a burst of laughter from the crowd. The officers laughed even more loudly, and praised their comrade-in-arms for having discountenanced the enemy so gloriously without becoming involved in a *scandal*. Oh, what a terrible thing a scandal is in Russia! It doesn't matter whether you behaved nobly or basely, whether you were right or wrong, whether you could have avoided it or not. If your name is involved in a scandal it doesn't make any difference: you will lose everything— social position, your career, the respect of your friends. To get involved in a scandal! There can be nothing worse than this, regardless of how the thing turns out. And personal notoriety is a sharp knife for society: you have made people talk about you for two days, and you will suffer twenty years for it. Although the judgment of public opinion is everywhere wrong, in Russia it operates on totally different principles than in the rest of Europe. In England, for example, bankruptcy represents a loss of honor which can never be repaired: it is sufficient motive for suicide. In Germany a person who has committed a rakish prank finds the doors of polite society forever closed to him. (I won't say anything about France: in Paris alone there are more public opinions than in all the rest of the world.) But in Russia? A confessed grafter is well received everywhere. He is excused with the phrase: "And who doesn't do it?" And a coward is everywhere treated with great affection because he is a peaceable chap. But the man involved in a scandal! There is no pity for him! The mamas will say, "God only knows what kind of a man he is!" And the papas will add, "He's a scoundrel!"

The officers finished drinking their tea without any fur-

ther disturbance, and went out. Pechorin was the last to
leave. On the steps, someone caught hold of his arm and
said, "I must have a word with you!" From the trembling
of his hand, Pechorin surmised that it was his recent
opponent. There was nothing for it: a scandal was un-
avoidable.

"By all means speak your piece," he answered casually,
"but not out here in the cold."

"In the theater lobby, then," the clerk said. And without further words, they went.

The second act had already begun: the lobby and the
broad staircases were empty. On the landing of a remote
staircase scarcely illuminated by a lamp some distance
away, they stopped. Pechorin crossed his arms on his chest,
leaned back against the iron balustrade, and after looking
his opponent over from head to foot, said with a frown,
"I'm ready to hear what you have to say."

"Sir—" The clerk's voice was trembling with rage. The
veins in his temples were swollen, and his lips had lost
their color. "Sir, you have offended me! You have mortally
offended me!"

"That is no secret to me," George answered, "and you
could have explained yourself in front of everyone. If you
had, my answer would have been the same as the one
I shall give you right now: What time would you prefer
for our duel? Now? Tomorrow? I believe I surmised your
intention. At any rate the breaking of the teacups was
not an accident. You wanted to start something, and you
began very cleverly," he added, with a mocking bow.

"Sir," the clerk said in a choking voice, "you almost

ran over me today. Yes, me, who stand here before you!
And you boast of it! You find it amusing! By what right?
Because you have a racehorse and a white-plumed cap?
Because you wear gold epaulettes? Do you think I'm not
just as much of a gentleman as you are? I am poor! I
have to go on foot. Naturally, this means I am not even
a human being, to say nothing of a gentleman. Ah, you
find it amusing! You thought I would sit quietly by and
listen to insolent remarks just because I had no money
I could throw on the table! No, never! Never will I forgive you!"

At this moment his flushed face had all the beauty of
a tempest. Pechorin looked at him with cool curiosity,
and then finally said, "Your comments are rather tedious.
Name the hour, and let us take our leave of each other.
You are shouting so loudly you'll arouse all the lackeys."
And indeed, some of them, who had been sleeping on
their masters' coats in the corridor outside the first tier,
had begun to raise their heads.

"What do I care about them? Let the whole world
hear me!"

"I'm afraid I don't share that opinion. If it is agreeable to you, I shall await you tomorrow with my second."
And Pechorin gave him his address.

"A duel! I see what you're getting at! A duel to the
death! And you think it will be enough for me to put
a ball of lead into your heart? A fine consolation! No,
I would like to see you live eternally, so that I could
take eternal revenge. A duel? No! That kind of success
is too uncertain."

"In that case," Pechorin replied with a shrug, "run along home, drink a glass of water, and go to bed." And he started to leave.

"No, wait!" the clerk said, regaining his composure somewhat. "Wait and hear me out! Do you think I'm a coward? That courage cannot exist without a display of spurs and epaulettes? Believe me, I value life and the future less than you do! My life is bitter, and I have no future. I am poor—poor as a church mouse. Not even once a year can I spend five rubles just for my own pleasure. I live on my salary, without friends or family except for my mother. She is old, and I am all she has— her providence and support. For me, she is both family and friends. Never in my life have I loved anyone but her. If she lost me, sir, she would die—if not from grief then from hunger." He paused. There were tears in his bloodshot eyes. "And you thought I would fight a duel with you?"

Pechorin said impatiently, "Then what is it, finally, that you want of me?"

"I want to make you regret what you have done."

"You seem to be forgetting that it was not I who started the quarrel."

"Do you really believe that to run a man down in the street is nothing? That it is a joke? Something amusing?"

"I promise you that I will whip my driver."

"Oh! I'm at the end of my patience!"

"Is that so? Then we shall duel."

The clerk did not answer. He covered his face with

his hands, his chest heaved, and his choked-off words showed his desperation. He seemed to be moaning. Finally he exclaimed, "No! I cannot! I will not be the cause of her death!" And he fled. Pechorin watched him leave, feeling sorry for him. Then he returned to his seat. The second act of *Fenella* was almost over. The artillery officer and his friend from the Preobrazhensky Regiment had not noticed his absence.

Chapter Three

Esteemed readers, all of you have seen *Fenella* a hundred times, and loudly applauded Novitskaya and Golland.[1] I shall therefore skip the remaining three acts and raise my curtain at the very moment when the curtain is being lowered at the Aleksandrinsky Theatre. I note merely that Pechorin paid little attention to the opera. He was preoccupied, and even forgot about the interesting box seat he had promised himself not to watch.

The noisy and contented crowd of operagoers was coming down the curved staircase toward the entrance. From below came the shouts of gendarmes and lackeys. The ladies, all bundled up and keeping close to the wall, screened by their husbands' and papas' bearskin coats from the bold looks of the young men, shivered with the cold—and smiled at everyone they knew. Officers and civilian fops with lorgnettes walked back and forth, the

[1] Maria Dmitrevna Novitskaya, a well-known singer, was a great favorite in the role of Fenella. The tenor, Golland, sang the role of Fenella's brother.

former clanking their swords and spurs, the latter stomping in their galoshes. The most distinguished ladies formed a separate group on the lower steps of the main staircase, smiling, talking in loud voices, and directing their gold lorgnettes toward the ladies of no distinction—the ordinary Russian gentlewomen. And they secretly envied one another. The distinguished ladies envied the beauty of the ordinary ones; and the ordinary ladies (alas!) envied the *hauteur* and brilliance of the distinguished ones.

Those in each group had their own escorts. The escorts of the ladies in the first group were grave and solemnly courteous, while those of the other ladies were obliging and sometimes clumsy. In the middle was a close-packed knot of people who did not belong to high society, and who were not acquainted with either of the other groups —a bunch of ordinary operagoers. The merchants and the common people were leaving through other doors. It was a picture in miniature of St. Petersburg society as a whole.

Pechorin, bundled up in his overcoat with his cap pulled down low over his eyes, was trying to get through to the door, when he found himself beside Lizaveta Negurova. He had replied to her meaningful smile with a curt bow, and was trying to move on, when he was detained by the following question: "Why are you so serious *Monsieur Georges*? Are you dissatisfied with the opera?"

"On the contrary, I called for Golland at the top of my voice."

"Novitskaya is very charming, don't you think?"

"You are quite right."

"You are enraptured with her."

"I am very seldom enraptured."

"At that rate you will never encourage anyone," she said with some irritation, attempting an ironic smile.

Pechorin answered casually, "I don't know anyone who requires my encouragement. And anyway, rapture is a childish thing . . ."

"Your ideas and the things you say have changed amazingly. Did this happen some time ago?"

"Yes, I assure you . . ." Pechorin wasn't listening. He was trying to peer through the motley wall of fur coats, cloaks, and caps. It seemed to him that out there, beyond the colonnade, he had caught a glimpse of a face that was familiar to him—especially familiar. At that moment a gendarme called out, "Prince Ligovskoy's carriage!" And a spindly-legged lackey repeated the words after him.

With a desperate effort, Pechorin fought his way through the crowd to the door. Looking past the four people still ahead of him, he glimpsed a pink cloak and heard the shuffling of a pair of little boots. The lackey helped the pink cloak into the elegant closed carriage. Then the bearskin coat clambered into it, and the doors slammed shut. "To Morskaya Street!" And they were gone.

The interesting carriage was followed by another—perhaps just as interesting, but not for Pechorin. He stood as if rooted to the spot. An agonizing thought had come to him: that box seat he had promised himself not to look at . . . Princess Ligovskaya had been sitting there, her little hand resting on the red velvet, and her eyes perhaps frequently coming to rest on him—and he had not even thought of turning around. The magnetic force in the glance of his beloved had not acted on his oxlike nerves. What folly! He would never forgive himself for this! In a state of deep vexation he went along the sidewalk until he found his sleigh. His driver was lying curled up under a fur sleigh robe. He gave him a tap to awaken him, and they drove home. But as for us, we shall turn our attention to Lizaveta Negurova, and follow her.

When she was seated in the carriage, her father began a long dissertation on the younger generation. "Take that Pechorin, for example," he said. "Instead of trying to be charming to me or Katenka"—Katenka, his wife, was fifty-five years old—"he even avoids looking at us! In my day, when a young man fell in love he tried to please the girl's parents, and all her other relatives besides. He wasn't always sitting in the corner whispering with her, and making eyes the way they do now. It's a shameful thing to see! And the girls are different, too. In the old days, when they heard something they shouldn't hear, they would blush. And that was it—you'd never get an answer out of them. But you, *matushka!* An old maid at the age of twenty-five, still running after everybody. I thought you wanted to get married!"

Lizaveta Nikolavna tried to answer, but tears started in her eyes and she could not say a word. Katerina Ivanovna interceded for her. "You're always scolding her, but it's no use! What's to be done when young men don't want to get married? The thing is not to let an opportunity pass by . . . Pechorin is a good catch. He comes from a good family. Why not him for a husband? A person can't stay at home forever. Good heavens, how much her dresses cost me! But you go on harping, 'Don't you want to get married? Don't you want to? Why, if people didn't get married, then . . .' And so on."

This conversation was repeated in one form or another every time the mother, father, and daughter were alone. The daughter remained silent; and what she felt in her heart at those moments, God only knows.

They arrived home. Katerina Ivanovna and her querulous husband went into their room, and the daughter went into hers. Her parents belonged to both the old century and the new one. The old ideas, half-forgotten and half-effaced by the new impressions from life in Petersburg and the influence of the social set to which Nikolai Petrovich belonged by virtue of his rank, emerged again only in moments of irritation or during a quarrel. They seemed to Nikolai Petrovich to be very powerful arguments indeed, because he remembered their formidable effect on his own mind in the days of his youth.

According to the government employees who worked in her husband's office, Katerina Ivanova was by no means a stupid woman. In the opinion of other old ladies, she was scheming and sly. To the younger party-going set, she was a mama who trusted her daughter to the point of blindness. What her character actually was, I have not yet been able to surmise. In describing her, I shall try only to combine and express together the three foregoing opinions. And if the portrait turns out to resemble the original, I promise to walk all the way to the Nevsky Monastery [2] to hear the monks chant.

As for Lizaveta Nikolavna, oh! (Exclamation point.)

[2] The Nevsky Monastery, or Aleksandro-Nevskaya Lavra, was in Lermontov's day located on the outskirts of Petersburg.

Wait! Now she has gone into her bedroom and rung for her maid, Marfusha, a fat, pock-marked wench! (Another exclamation point.) I would not like my wife or fiancée to have a fat, pock-marked maid. I cannot bear fat, pock-marked maids with their hair greased down with smelly oil or smoothed down with kvass, so that it becomes sticky and has a reddish color; with hands as rough and coarse as yesterday's rye bread; with sleepy eyes; with feet scuffing along in slippers minus their straps; with a heavy gait; and (worst of all) a quadrangular figure wrapped up in a housedress which is narrower at the bottom than at the top. Such a maid, sitting at her work in the rear room of a respectable house, is like a crocodile at the bottom of a clear American well.[3] Such a maid is like a grease spot showing through the bright figures on a newly-dyed dress: she raises gloomy doubts about the domestic life of her master and mistress. Dear friends, may God grant that you never fall in love with a girl who has such a maid! If you share my opinion, this would destroy your enchantment forever.

Lizaveta Nikolavna told the maid to remove her slippers and stockings and to undo her corset. She herself, sitting on the bed, carelessly tossed her hat onto the dressing table, and her dark hair fell over her shoulders. But I shall not continue with the description: nobody is inter-

---

[3] 'Well' is here used in the sense of "natural spring and pool" (Webster). Lermontov got both his "American well" and his "crocodile" from Chateaubriand. Cf., from *Atala*: *Le coeur le plus serein en apparence ressemble au puits naturel de la savane Alachua: la surface en paroit calme et pure, mais quand vous regardez au fond du bassin, vous apercevez un large crocodile que le puits nourrit dans ses eaux.*

ested in admiring faded charms—a thin neck with prominent veins, and thin shoulders with red marks on them
from the tight dress. Everybody, I suppose, has seen
enough of such things.

Lizaveta Nikolavna lay down on the bed, moved the
candle on the bedside table nearer to her, and opened a
French novel. Marfusha left the room, and silence
reigned. The melancholy young lady let the book fall
from her hands, sighed, and gave herself over to her
musings.

Naturally, no faded beauty ever confided to me her
meditations and the feelings which stirred her bosom
after a long soirée or ball when, alone in her room, she
summoned up her entire past, recalling all of the declarations of love she had received at one time or another with
feigned indifference, a feigned smile, or genuine pleasure
—declarations which had no other consequences for her
but ten lines in an album or a vindictive epigram from
a rejected admirer, spoken as he passed behind the back
of her chair during a long mazurka. But I should imagine
that these musings must be painful and unbearable for her
pride and her heart—if indeed she really has a heart. For
natural history has now been enriched with a new class of
very charming and beautiful creatures; namely, the class of
women who have no heart.

In order more easily to surmise what Lizaveta Nikolavna
deigned to think about, I am obliged, much to my regret,
to tell you certain particulars of her life. And this is all
the more necessary in order to explain the subsequent
events.

She was born in Petersburg, and never went outside of that city. True, she once went to the seashore at Revel for two months. But you know yourself that Revel is not Russia; and so there was no change in the direction of her Petersburg upbringing.

French governesses have gone somewhat out of fashion in Russia; and in Petersburg there are none of them at all. Her parents were not in a position to hire an English governess, because they are expensive. There were also some difficulties involved in hiring a German woman, because God knows what kind they might have got—we have so many of them, here, of all varieties.

And so Elizaveta Nikolavna was left with no governess at all. She learned French from her mama; and even more from the guests, because from the time she was a little girl she spent her days in the drawing room, sitting next to her mother and hearing anything and everything. When she was thirteen, an outside tutor was engaged for her. She completed her French course in one year, and then her social education was begun. She had a grand piano in her room, but when she played it nobody heard her. She learned to dance at balls given for young people. She began to read novels as soon as she had learned the parts of speech; and she read them with astonishing rapidity. Meantime, her father had come into a substantial inheritance, and shortly thereafter he was given a good position. He began to live on a larger scale. When Elizaveta was fifteen years old she was presented to society, and made to pass for seventeen. This arbitrary age remained unchanged until she was twenty-five. Seventeen is the freezing point: those seventeen years stretch as easily as elastic suspenders.

Lizaveta Nikolavna was rather attractive, and very interesting-looking. A pallid complexion and thinness are interesting because French girls are pallid and English girls are thin. (It should be noted that the charm of pallor and thinness exists only in the imagination of the ladies, and that our men indulge this opinion only by way of compliancy and in order to avoid the accusation that they are ignorant and have so-called "barrack-room manners.")

When Elizaveta Nikolavna first made her appearance in society she had her admirers. All of them were the kind of young men who are always applauding a new vaudeville show or rushing off to hear a new opera singer, and who read only the latest novels. They were followed by others who flirted with her in order to arouse the jealousy of a mistress who had grown cool, or to wound the vanity of a hard-hearted beauty. Next came a third species of admirers: young men who became enamored for want of anything else to do, so that they could pass the evening pleasantly; because Lizaveta Nikolavna had acquired skill in social conversation and was very obliging, somewhat given to mockery, and a bit dreamy. Some of these gallants fell in love with her in dead earnest, and asked for her hand. But she wanted to attempt the flattering role of the unyielding woman . . . and besides, all of them were extremely boring. So she refused them. One of them, in his despair, was ill for a long time; others found quick consolation. Meanwhile, time passed, and she became an experienced and audacious old maid:

she would look everyone over with her lorgnette. Her behavior was very bold; and she never blushed at a double-entendre or suggestive glance. She began to be courted by a set of rosy-cheeked youths trying their strength in verbal skirmishes, who dedicated to her their first attempts at amorous eloquence. But alas! They offered even less hopes than all of the others. With annoyance, and at the same time a secret satisfaction, she would cut short their effusions of eloquence with an acid witticism; and they soon realized she was a strange and unconquerable women. So the swarm of wooers flew off to other fields. And finally Lizaveta Nikolavna reached that period in her life which is most anguishing and dangerous to the heart of a woman whose beauty has faded.

She had reached that age when to flirt with her was no longer honorable, and to fall in love with her was difficult—that age when any frivolous or indifferent fop felt no real harm was done if he feigned a deep passion for her so that later, just for a laugh, he might compromise the young lady in the eyes of her friends, with the idea of adding to his own importance: to assure everybody that she was crazy about him, and try to show that he pitied her and didn't know how to get rid of her; to whisper sweet nothings to her, and then make caustic remarks aloud. The poor girl, with a premonition that this was to be her last admirer, would try to keep the rogue's affections—not out of love, but simply to save her own pride. But in vain: her troubles would only increase. And finally (alas!) after this period there remained only dreams of a husband—any husband. Just dreams . . .

Lizaveta Nikolavna was just entering this period. But the last blow was delivered to her, not by an indifferent fop and not by a heartless rogue. Here is what happened.

A year and a half before, Pechorin had still been a rather new arrival in society. In order to give himself some kind of standing he had to acquire what some people call a worldly reputation; that is, to become known as a man who could do evil when the fancy took him. For some time he sought in vain for a footstool upon which he could climb to compel the attention of society. To become the lover of a famous beauty would have been too difficult for a beginner; and he could not bring himself to compromise a young and innocent girl. Therefore he chose Lizaveta Nikolavna, who was neither one nor the other, as his instrument. What else could you expect? In our pathetic society the phrase, "He ruined so many reputations" means almost the same thing as "He won such-and-such a number of battles."

He and Lizaveta Nikolavna had been acquainted with each other for a long time. They exchanged greetings whenever they met in public. Having drawn up his plan, Pechorin went to a certain ball where he knew he would meet her. He observed her carefully and noticed that no one asked her to dance the mazurka. The musicians were given the signal to begin; and the ladies' escorts noisily moved the chairs about, placing them in a circle. Lizaveta Nikolavna went to the powder room in order to conceal her vexation. Pechorin waited for her near the door. When she returned they had already begun to dance the second figure. Pechorin went up to her eagerly. "Where have you been?" he asked. "I have been looking for you everywhere. I even set up the chairs, so great was my hope that you would not refuse me."

"How self-assured you are!" Unexpected pleasure shone in her eyes.

"But you will not punish me too severely for being self-assured?"

Without answering, she followed him.

They continued their conversation throughout the entire dance. It sparkled with jokes and epigrams, and touched upon everything—even the metaphysics of love. Pechorin did not spare a one of her young, fresh-complexioned rivals. After the *souper* he sat down beside her, and the conversation was carried further and further, so that at least he almost told her that he adored her to the point of madness (ambiguously, of course). A great stride had been taken, and he went home content with his evening.

During the next few weeks they met at various soirees. It goes without saying that he tirelessly sought out these meetings, and for her part, she at least did not avoid them. In a word, he was following in the tracks of her former admirers and behaving as form demanded, in the classical manner. Before long everyone began to notice their constant attraction for each other as a new and completely original phenomenon in our cold society. Pechorin avoided immodest questions, and instead behaved very openly. Lizaveta Nikolavna was also very content with this, since she hoped to draw him on further and further and then, as our dear old mothers used to say, marry him for herself. Her parents, having no idea of what he was like, simply ignored the usual forms and invited him to call at their home so that they could get to know him better. Many others began to make fun of him as a future fiancé. And good friends of his began to warn him to avoid a reckless step which he had no intention of taking. From all this he concluded that a decisive crisis had arrived.

Baron _____ was giving a brilliant ball. Pechorin, as usual, danced the first quadrille with Elizaveta Nikolavna.

"How pretty the younger R____ sister looks tonight!" Elizaveta remarked.

Pechorin fixed his eyeglass on the young beauty, studied her for a long time in silence, and then finally said, "Yes, she is beautiful. How tastefully those bright red flowers are arranged in her thick blonde hair. I have promised myself faithfully to dance with her tonight, just because you find her charming. When I want to do something to please you, I am very quick to surmise, am I not?"

"Oh, you are very obliging, no doubt about it!" she answered, flaring up suddenly.

At that moment the music stopped and the first quadrille was over. Bowing very politely, Pechorin took his leave. For the remainder of the evening he either danced with R____, or stood near her chair, trying to talk as much as possible and appear as content as possible—although, just between you and me, the little R____ girl was very simple-minded and scarcely listened to him. But since he talked a great deal, she concluded that Pechorin was a very nice young man.

After the mazurka she went up to Elizaveta Nikolavna, and the latter asked her with an ironic smile, "How do you like your constant companion of the evening?"

"*Il est très aimable,*" answered R____.

This was a hard blow for Elizaveta Nikolavna, who felt that she was losing her last suitor, since all of the other young men, seeing that Pechorin was paying attention only to her, had abandoned her entirely.

And, as a matter of fact, from that evening on, Pechorin began to be more cool and indifferent toward her. It was quite obvious that he was subjecting her to those small annoyances that everyone notices but for which one cannot demand satisfaction. When talking with other young ladies he would express his pity for her in a humiliating way. She, on the contrary, in a miscalculated attempt to touch his vanity, would tell her friends, in strictest secrecy, of her very pure and genuine love for him. But in vain: he merely enjoyed an additional measure of triumph; while she, by dint of affirming it to others, gradually came to believe that she did in fact love him. Her parents, who in their role of impartial onlookers were more perceptive, began to warn her. "You've wasted a whole year now, *matushka*. You've turned down one suitor with twenty thousand rubles a year! To be sure, he is old and paralyzed. But what do the young men of today amount to? Your Pechorin is a fine one! We knew all along that he wouldn't marry you. For that matter, his mother won't let him marry. So what has happened? Now he's making fun of you!"

It goes without saying that words like these do not

assuage either wounded pride or a deceived heart. Lizaveta Nikolavna sensed their truth; but that truth was no
longer new to her. Whoever has pursued any goal for a
long time, and made many sacrifices for it, finds it hard
to give up the pursuit; and if that goal involves the last
hopes of a faded youth, to give it up is impossible. Such
was the situation in which we left Lizaveta Nikolavna
when she had returned from the opera and lain down on
her bed with the book in her hands, and with thoughts
that roamed into the past and the future.

Bored from having read the same page over ten times,
she impatiently tossed the book onto the bedside table.
Suddenly she noticed a letter addressed to her, bearing
the stamp of the city post office.

Some inner sense told her not to unseal the mysterious
envelope. But curiosity prevailed, and she tore it open
with trembling hands. She moved the candle closer, and
with eager eyes scanned the first few lines. The letter was
written in an obviously distorted hand, as though the
writer had been afraid that the very characters would
betray him. In lieu of a signature there were some hiero-
glyph-like doodles very much resembling those spots on
the moon to which ignorant people attribute symbolic
meanings. Here is the letter, word for word.

Milostivaya Gosudarynya!
You do not know me, but I know you. We have met often. The
story of your life is as familiar to me as my notebook, but you have
never heard my name. I take an interest in you precisely because
you have never paid any attention to me. Moreover, I am very content with myself at the moment, and determined to do a good deed.

I happen to know that you like Pechorin and are trying in every way to arouse in him feelings which he never dreamed of having. He has been toying with your feelings. He is unworthy of you. And he loves another woman. All your efforts will only serve to bring on your own ruin. Society is already pointing the finger of scorn at you, and soon it will abandon you altogether.

No prospect of personal benefit prompted me to offer you such bold and incautious advice. In order to convince you of my disinterestedness, I swear to you that you will never know my name.

As a consequence of which I remain,

Your most devoted servant,
Doodles

Another young lady might have been thrown into hysteria by such a letter. But the blow which struck Lizaveta Nikolavna in the depths of her heart did not affect her nerves: she merely paled, hastily burned the letter, and blew its light ashes to the floor.

Then she put out the candle and turned her face toward the wall. She seemed to be crying—but so softly that if you had been standing at the head of her bed you would have thought she was sleeping peacefully and quietly.

When she arose the next morning she was even paler than usual. At ten o'clock she went into the sitting room and served tea herself, as usual. When they got up from the table her father left for his office, her mother sat down to her work, and Lizaveta went to her own room. As she was passing through the main hallway she met a servant.

"Where are you going?" she asked.

"To announce a caller."

"Who is it?"

"That officer, Pechorin."

"Where is he?"

"He's waiting outside."

Lizaveta Nikolavna blushed, and grew pale again. Then in a curt voice she said to the servant, "Tell him that there is no one at home. And if he comes back again," she added, uttering the last phrase as if with difficulty, "do not receive him!"

The servant bowed and left. Lizaveta ran headlong to her own room.

Chapter Four

As you might well imagine, Pechorin was not surprised when he was refused admission in such a decisive manner: he was prepared for this dénouement, and had even desired it. He set off along Morskaya Street, the runners of his sleigh gliding rapidly over the powdery snow. It was a cloudy morning, and gave promise of an imminent thaw. Many inhabitants of Petersburg who have passed their childhood in a different climate have been strangely affected by the weather here. A kind of melancholy indifference, like that with which our northern sun turns away from this ungrateful part of the earth, creeps into the soul and induces a torpor in all the vital organs. At such times, the heart is incapable of enthusiasm, and the mind of reflection.

This was the mood in which Pechorin found himself. His frivolous undertaking had been crowned by an unexpected measure of success; yet he could not even take pleasure in it. Moreover, in a few minutes he was to see the woman who had constantly been the object of his reveries for the past several years—a woman to whom he was bound by the past, and for whom he was ready to give his whole future. And yet his heart did not tremble from impatience, fear, or hope. The only indications of an imminent storm within were a kind of morbid numbness—a kind of dullness and sluggishness of thought, which like heavy clouds had settled upon his mind. Remembering his past ardor, he was vexed by his present placidity.

His sleigh stopped in front of the house, and he went up to the door and took hold of the knob. But before he opened it, the past slipped into his imagination like a dream, and a number of feelings suddenly and tumultuously came awake in his soul. He himself was frightened by the loud beating of his heart, as the sleepy inhabitants of a city are frightened by the sound of the night alarm. Whatever were his intentions, fears, and hopes, God only knows; but he was ready to take a decisive step—to give a new direction to his life. Finally, the door was opened and he went slowly up a broad staircase. In response to the porter's question, he asked whether Princess Ligovskaya was at home.

"Prince Ligovskoy is at home," the porter said.

"And the Princess?"

"The Princess, too."

Pechorin gave his name, and the porter went off to announce him.

Pechorin looked curiously through the half-opened door leading into the reception room, trying to glean from the way it was arranged, at least a hint as to the family life of the Ligovskoys. But alas! In Petersburg, all reception rooms are the same, like all smiles and all greetings. Only the study will sometimes reveal domestic secrets. But for mere visitors, the study is as impenetrable as the heart. However, from his brief exchange with the porter it was clear to Pechorin that the chief personage in the household was the prince. It's strange, he thought. She married an old, unpleasant, and mediocre man, presumably in order to have her own way. And yet, if I have guessed correctly, she voluntarily exchanged one kind of servitude for another. What, then, was her aim? What was the reason? . . . Surely she cannot love him. I'll wager my life on that.

At this moment the porter returned and solemnly announced: "Please come in. The prince is in the drawing room."

Pechorin walked slowly through the reception room. His vision blurred, and the blood rushed to his heart. He felt himself growing pale as he entered the drawing room. A young woman in a satin housecoat and a white silk cap was sitting in a relaxed posture on the divan. Near her, in an armchair, was a fat, bald gentleman wearing a regulation frock coat. He had huge, bloodshot eyes and the smile on his face was infinitely broad. Another man in a tail coat, rather lean, with close-cropped hair, sagging jowls, and a rather unpleasant expression on his face, was standing by the window. He was looking at a newspaper and did not even turn around when the young officer entered. This was Prince Stepan Stepanovich himself.

The young woman arose quickly, turned to Pechorin with a kind of vague welcome, and then went over to the prince and said, "*Mon ami*, this is Monsieur Pechorin, an old friend of our family. Monsieur Pechorin, I'd like you to meet my husband."

Prince Ligovskoy dropped his newspaper on the window-sill, bowed, and made an effort at saying something, but uttered only a few broken phrases. "Of course. Delighted . . . my wife's family . . . you are so kind . . . I promised myself I would . . . Your mother is a distinguished lady. I had the honor of calling at the house yesterday with my wife."

"My mother wanted to call on you today, and bring my sister. But she is feeling a bit ill, and asked me to convey her regards."

Pechorin did not know what he was saying. He regained his composure, and realizing that he had said something stupid, assumed a cold and affected manner. Princess Ligovskaya no doubt had the impression that with this phrase he was trying to explain the reason for his visit, as though he had come against his own will. The expression on her face became as strained as his own. She suspected an intention to reproach her, and her cheeks were on the point of flushing. But she turned quickly and said something to the fat gentleman, who laughed and said loudly, "Oh, yes!" Then she asked Pechorin to sit down, and she herself took her former place on the divan. Prince Ligovskoy picked up his newspaper again.

Princess Vera Dmitrevna was a woman of twenty-two. She was of medium height and blonde, with dark eyes, which lent her an unusual kind of charm and, by setting her distinctly apart from other women, ruled out any comparisons—which might not perhaps have been in her favor. She was not a beautiful woman, although her features were quite regular. The oval of her face was perfectly Greek, and the pellucid quality of her skin was unusual. The constant mobility of her features, apparently incompatible with their rather sharply defined contours, was such that she did not at all times appear attractive to everyone. And yet a person accustomed to following these rapid changes of expression, could have discerned in them an unusually spirited temperament and a constant nervous excitability, promising much pleasure to a perceptive lover. Her figure was supple, her movements unhurried and graceful. Seeing her for the first time you would have said, if you were an experienced observer, that she was a woman of firm, and resolute character, rather cold, who had the strength of her own convictions and was ready to sacrifice her happiness to the rules of society, though not to mere gossip. But if you had seen her in a moment of passion or excitement you would have said something quite different. Or rather, you would not have known what to say at all.

For several minutes she and Pechorin sat facing each other in a silence which was difficult for both of them. The fat gentleman, who for some reason or other was a baron, took advantage of this interval of time to explain in detail his kinship with the Prussian Ambassador. Vera, by means of various questions, very skillfully obliged the baron to expand his remarks even further. George watched her closely, trying vainly to surmise her innermost thoughts. He could see plainly that she was not quite herself—

that she was anxious and disturbed. At times her eyes would take on a dull cast, then they would sparkle again. Her lips would smile, then tauten; and her cheeks would flush and grow pale by turns. What was the cause of this anxiety? Perhaps a quarrel between husband and wife just before Pechorin's arrival—since it was obvious that Prince Ligovskoy was out of sorts. Perhaps the joy and agitation of Vera's reborn (or only just awakened) love for himself. Or perhaps her unpleasant feelings at meeting, again, a man who knew certain secrets of her life and heart— who had the right to reproach her, and was perhaps ready to do so.

Pechorin, who was not accustomed to interpreting women's glances and feelings in his own favor, decided that the last possibility was the most likely one. And out of pride he resolved to show that he, too, had forgotten the past and rejoiced in her happiness. But, quite against his will, the sound of his voice betrayed his wounded feelings.

When he started to speak, Vera turned quickly away from the baron, leaving the latter with his mouth hanging open, just on the point of uttering his most important and convincing conclusion.

"Princess," George said, "you must forgive me. I have not yet congratulated you . . . upon your title. Believe me, that was my intention in calling upon you so promptly. But when I came in just now I was so surprised at seeing how much you had changed, that I must admit I neglected that point of etiquette."

"I have aged, have I not?" Vera asked, turning her head toward her right shoulder.

"Oh, you are joking! People don't age when they are happy. On the contrary, you have gained weight. You—"

"Of course I am very happy," she broke in.

"That's what everyone is saying. Many young ladies envy you. For that matter, you are so sensible that you couldn't have failed to make such a worthy choice. Everyone is enraptured by your husband's charm, intelligence, and talents." The baron nodded his head in agreement. Vera almost smiled; then a sudden look of annoyance came over her face.

"Monsieur Pechorin, I will repay your compliment with another. You, too, have changed for the better."

"What can I say? Time is all-powerful. Even our clothes have undergone marvelous changes, like ourselves. Now you are wearing a white silk cap. And instead of a student's coat, or the frock coat of a Moscow adolescent, I am wearing a uniform with epaulettes. That is no doubt why I have the honor of being more to your liking now than in the past. You have become so accustomed to glitter!"

Vera was eager to take revenge for this sally. "Perfect!" she exclaimed. "You have guessed it. Indeed, for us poor Muscovites a Guardsman's uniform is a real rarity!" She smiled mockingly. The baron laughed, and Pechorin felt a sudden anger toward him.

"Princess," he said, "you have such a zealous ally that I must admit to defeat. I am convinced that the baron is ready, at a given signal, to crush me with all of his weight."

The baron did not understand Russian very well, although he had been born in Russia. He laughed even more loudly than before, taking Pechorin's remark as a compliment to himself as well as to Vera. Pechorin shrugged his shoulders, and the conversation again lagged. Fortunately, Prince Ligovskoy came over to them, holding a newspaper with an important air.

"Here is something that should interest you," he said to his wife. "A new shop has opened on Nevsky Prospect. I will show you," he said, turning to his guests, "the Petersburg gift I bought for my wife yesterday. A pair of earrings. Everyone says they are very fashionable, but my wife disagrees. I would like to have your opinion."

He went into the next room and returned with a morocco-leather case. To Pechorin, the word 'wife,' which Prince Ligovskoy repeated so frequently, had a rather crude and unpleasant sound. He had recognized, as soon as the prince began to speak, that he was a man of limited intelligence. And now he was convinced that the man was not even socially competent.

The earrings were passed from hand to hand, and the baron uttered some prolonged exclamations about them. Then Pechorin began to examine them in a perfunctory manner.

"What do you think?" asked Prince Ligovskoy, ducking his chin behind his foulard and tugging at his starched collar with one hand. "How much do you think I paid for them? Guess!"

The earrings were worth eighty rubles at the very most, and had been bought for seventy-five. Pechorin deliberately said, "One hundred and fifty." Prince Ligovskoy was embarrassed. He was ashamed to tell the truth, so he said nothing. Sitting down on the divan, he gave Pechorin a very disagreeable look.

The conversation now developed into a general exchange of the latest events in St. Petersburg and news from Moscow. The prince, who had brightened up a bit, declared very frankly that had it not been for his lawsuit he never would have left Moscow and the English Club there—adding that the English Club in Petersburg was as nothing compared to the one in Moscow. Finally, Pechorin rose to take his leave. He had already reached the door when Vera suddenly got up from her place and most persuasively asked him not to forget to kiss her dear Varenka for her a hundred times—even a thousand times. Pechorin was tempted to tell her that he could not transmit verbal kisses. But he wasn't up to making jokes, so he merely bowed again, very politely. Vera gave him a meaningless smile—the kind of smile one sees on the face of a ballerina who has just completed a pirouette.

He left the room with a feeling of bitter foreboding. As he was passing through the reception hall, he stopped and turned. Vera was standing in the doorway, watching him go. When she saw him turn, she disappeared.

It's strange, he thought, as he got into his sleigh. There was a time when I could read all of her thoughts on her face, just as clearly as my own handwriting. But now I don't understand her—I don't understand her at all.

Chapter Five

Until he was nineteen, Pechorin had lived in Moscow. From early childhood he had moved about from one boarding school to another. Finally, he had crowned his wanderings by matriculating at the university, according to the wishes of his very wise mama. He had become so fond of roaming about, that if he had lived in Germany he would have become a wandering student. But just tell me, for God's sake: How is it possible, in Russia, to be the wandering master of three thousand serfs and the wandering nephew of twenty thousand Moscow aunts? And so his wanderings were limited to trips (with a band of worthless fellows like himself) to the Petrovsky, the Sokolniki, and the Marina woods. It can well be imagined that they did not take with them their notebooks and textbooks, lest they should appear to be bookworms. Pechorin's friends (he did not have a great many, by the way) were all young fellows who had made his acquaintance in society, since in those days the students were the only available beaux for the Moscow belles, who could not help sighing for epaulettes and tassels of gold braid, never suspecting that in our time these glittering displays have lost the importance they once had.

Pechorin and his friends also put in their appearance on all festive occasions. Arm-in-arm, they would stroll through the rows of carriages, to the great consternation of the policemen. If you met one of these young fellows you could safely bet, with your eyes closed, that the others would appear forwith. In Moscow, where the name is still in style, they were called *la bande joyeuse*.

Examination time was drawing near for Pechorin. For a year he had hardly gone to a lecture; and now he intended to sacrifice a few nights to his studies and catch up, in one leap, with his classmates. But a situation suddenly developed which prevented him from carrying out this heroic intention. His mother, Tatyana Petrovna, often held children's soirees for her little girl. These soirees were also attended by young ladies and over-ripe virgins eager for any kind of evening entertainment. At nine o'clock the children were put to bed, and the adults took their places on the dance floor.

These evenings were often attended by a certain Mr. R____ and his daughter. They were old acquaintances of Tatyana Petrovna, and even distantly related to her. The daughter, in those days, was known simply as Verochka. To George, who had become used to seeing her quite often, there was nothing particularly remarkable about her. For her part, she avoided talking with him. Then one time a large company was assembled to go to the Simonov Monastery for vespers and matins—to hear the monks chant, and to have an outing. It was in the spring. They got into their carriages, arranged in two long lines with six horses to each, and set off from the Arbat in a merry caravan. The sun was setting behind the Sparrow Hills, and the evening was indeed beautiful.

As it happened, George was seated next to Verochka. At first this displeased him. The freshness and modesty of the seventeen-year-old girl seemed to him sure indications of coldness and a kind of saccharine innocence of the heart. Every one of us, at nineteen, has had the experience of rushing headlong after a fading coquette [1] whose words and glances were full of promises, but whose soul was like the prettily painted coffins in the parable: on the outside, alluring glitter; on the inside, death and ashes.

When they had left the outskirts of the city and the merry travelers were refreshed by the soft evening air, George struck up a conversation with Verochka. Her talk was unaffected, lively, and rather free. She was somewhat inclined to dreaminess, but did not make a display of it. Rather, she was embarrassed by it, as a weakness. George's own opinions, in those days, were outspoken and full of contradictions, although original—something generally true of the opinions of young men reared in Moscow and used to developing their ideas without external compulsion.

Finally, they reached the monastery. While waiting for the service to begin, they walked around looking at the walls and the cemetery. And they climbed up to the platform of the Western tower—that same platform from which, in olden times, our forefathers watched the movements of the enemy, and where "the last princely page" [1] discovered so belatedly his real name, his fate, and his name as an exile. George made sure not to lag behind Verochka, because it would have been awkward to separate from her before they had finished their talk; and it was

[1] *Sic*—though perhaps "neo-nymphet" would be closer to the mark.—Ed.
[1] The son of Princess Sofia Alekseyevna (Romanova), regent for seven years (1682–89) during the minority of Peter the Great, by Prince Basil Golitsyn; hero of an historical novel, *The Last Princely Page*, by I. I. Lazhechnikov (1833).

talk of such a kind that it could have gone on indefinitely. It did in fact continue throughout the midnight Mass, except for those moments when the divine choir of monks and the voice of Father Viktor plunged the two of them into wordless rapture. After such moments, however, their stimulated imaginations and the feelings aroused by the music, provided new food for thought and conversation.

After the Mass they all strolled about again. Then they returned to the city, very late, in the same order in which they had left. During the whole of the next day George kept thinking of that evening. Then he went over to the R——'s to talk about it and relate his impressions to the one with whom he had shared them. His visits became more and more frequent and prolonged. But since the two families were on very close terms, these visits did not arouse any suspicions. After an entire month had passed in this way, he and Verochka were convinced that they were madly in love with each other. At that age, when passion is a pleasure unalloyed by cares, anxiety, or remorse, it is very easy to become convinced of anything at all.

George had a wealthy aunt who was likewise related to the R——s. The aunt invited both families to spend a week or two at her home outside of Moscow. Her house was huge, and the grounds were spacious: in short, it offered every advantage. George and Verochka often went walking together, and this drew them even closer. Despite the crowd of governesses and the aunt's children, they somehow found a way to be alone. It is a way rather easily found, incidentally, if both parties are willing.

Meantime, examinations were being held at the university. George did not put in an appearance and, naturally, he received no diploma. But he was not worried about the future. He had assured his mother that the examinations had been postponed for three weeks, and that he knew all of his subjects well.

The evening walks inevitably resulted in a declaration of love, followed by oaths of fidelity. Finally, when the two weeks were over, it was necessary to return to Moscow. On the evening before the fateful day, George and Verochka were standing on the balcony. They were standing very close together: some mysterious spirit had brought their lips and hands together in a wordless pressure, a wordless kiss! They were frightened of their own selves. And although George, aided by his friends, had at an early age made his debut in the seductive world of debauchery, the honor of a chaste young girl was still something sacred to him. The next day, as they were getting into their carriages, they took leave of each other very politely, as before. But Verochka blushed, and her eyes shone.

George's deceit was discovered as soon as they reached Moscow. Tatyana Petrovna's despair was frightful, and her scolding never ceased. George, submissive and silent, listened through the whole thing like a stoic. But, invisible to him, a thunderhead was gathering above him. The committee of uncles and aunts had decided that he should be sent to Petersburg and enrolled in the Cavalry Cadet School. They saw no other salvation for him. At the cadet school, they said, he would be licked into shape and taught discipline.

The campaign [2] against Poland was being organized at this time, and all the young men were rushing to find a place in a regiment. It would have been disadvantageous for George to enter the cadet school, since junior cadets were not allowed to go on campaign. Virtually on his knees, he begged his mother's permission to join the X—— Regiment of Hussars, then encamped near Moscow. After much crying and sighing on her part, he obtained her blessing. But the most difficult thing yet remained to be done: he had to explain all this to Verochka. He was still so naïve that he feared she would be crushed by the unexpected news. But she heard him out in silence and fixed him with a look of reproach, refusing to believe that any circumstances whatsoever could compel him to part from her. By oaths and promises, she was appeased.

A few days later George went to the R——'s house for a final leave-taking. Verochka was very pale. He did not remain long in the drawing room. But when he left, she ran through the other door and met him in the reception room. Seizing his hand, she squeezed it tightly and said in a faltering voice, "I will never belong to another." The poor girl was trembling all over. Those feelings were so new to her; she was so fearful of losing her friend; and she was so sure of her own heart! Planting a burning kiss on her cool, virginal brow, George sat her down in a chair, ran rapidly down the stairs, and hurried home. That evening one of the R——'s servants came to Tatyana Petrovna's to ask for some spirits and a bottle of some kind of

[2] Of 1830.

medicine, because "the young mistress is very sick and has fainted two or three times." This was a terrible blow to George, and he did not sleep all that night. By dawn of the next day he was in an open carriage and on his way to the regiment.

Up to this point, dear readers, you have seen that the love between my hero and heroine has not deviated from the general rules for all novels and all beginning love affairs. But later on—oh! Later on you will see and hear some marvelous things!

During the campaign Pechorin distinguished himself, like every Russian officer, and fought bravely, like every Russian soldier. He flirted with a good many Polish girls; but the moment of his parting from Verochka, and the charming image of her, constantly troubled his imagination. It was a strange business! He had left with the firm intention of forgetting her, and things had turned out exactly the opposite (which almost always happens in such cases). Moreover, Pechorin had a most unfortunate temperament: impressions which at first were superficial, would gradually be engraved ever more deeply in his mind. So that, as time went on, his love for Verochka came to acquire over his heart a right of seniority—the most sacred of all rights of mankind.

After the capture of Warsaw he was transferred to the Guards, and his mother and sister came to live in Petersburg. Varenka brought greetings from her "dear Verochka," as she called her—nothing more than greetings. Pechorin was embittered by this. (He did not yet understand women.) His secret bitterness was one of the reasons why he began to court Lizaveta Negurova. Apparently, Verochka got wind of it. Some eighteen months later he learned that she had married. And two years after that she came to Petersburg, no longer as Verochka but as Princess Ligovskaya, the wife of Prince Stepan Stepanych.

It was at this point, if I recall correctly, that we stopped in the preceding chapter.

Chapter Six

Three days after Pechorin's visit to the Ligovskoys, Tatyana Petrovna invited several friends and relatives for dinner. As might have been expected, Prince Stepan Stepanych Ligovskoy and his wife were among those invited.

Pechorin was sitting in his study, about to dress for dinner, when an artillery officer came in. "Ah, Branitsky!" Pechorin exclaimed. "I'm very glad you came just at the right time! You must by all means dine with us. Just imagine: our house is full of young girls, and I alone have been offered up as a sacrifice. You know all of them. Please do me the favor of staying to dinner!"

"Judging from your persuasiveness," Branitsky answered, "you seem to be anticipating a refusal."

"No," Pechorin said, "you dare not refuse!" He rang for a servant and ordered Branitsky's sleigh sent home.

I shall not relate the rest of their talk, since it was aimless and insignificant, like the talk of all young men with time on their hands. For that matter, I wish you would tell me what young men *should* talk about. The supply of news is quickly exhausted; prudence rules out any mention of politics; of service matters there is too much talk while on duty, anyway; and women, in our barbarous age, have lost half of their former universal influence. As for falling in love, it seems embarrassing; and to talk about it is ludicrous.

When several of the guests had arrived, Pechorin and Branitsky went down to the drawing room. Games of whist were in progress at three tables. While the mamas counted trumps, their daughters, seated around a small table, talked of the latest ball and the latest fashions. The two officers came up to them, and Branitsky skillfully enlivened their small group with some casual chit-chat. Pechorin was pensive. He had long ago noticed that Branitsky was courting his sister. And not having given any close study to the ultimate consequences, he had not troubled his friend with supervision, or his sister with embarrassing questions. For Varenka it was very pleasant that such a clever young man should conspicuously single her out from the others. After all, she had not even come out yet.

Little by little the guests assembled. Prince and Princess Ligovskoy were among the last to arrive. Varenka ran to meet her old friend, and Vera kissed her with a protective air. Soon everyone was seated at the dinner table.

The dining room was elegantly furnished. The walls were hung with pictures in huge gold frames. The somber tones of the old-style paintings contrasted sharply with the general decor of the room, which was light, like everything else in the latest fashion. Some of the figures in these paintings were half-nude; others were artistically draped in Greek mantles or Spanish costumes, with broad-brimmed plumed hats, slashed sleeves, and sumptuous ruffles. Put on canvas by the artist's hand at the most brilliant moment in their mythological or feudal lives, they seemed to be looking sternly at the figures in this room, lighted by a hundred candles, who had no thought for the future and even less for the past: persons who had assembled for a lavish dinner, not so much to enjoy the pleasures bestowed by luxury as for other reasons—some of them, in order to satisfy the vanity of wealth or intellect; others out of curiosity, for reasons of propriety, or for purposes cloaked in mystery. In the dress of these persons seated so decorously at the long table set with porcelain and silver service, and in their ideas as well, all ages were intermingled. In their dress, the most hoary antiquity mingled with the latest notions of Parisian *modistes:* Greek coiffures, crowned with garlands of artificial flowers; Gothic earrings; Jewish turbans; even upswept coiffures *à la chinoise;* curls *à la Sévigné;* bouffant dresses resembling farthingales; and sleeves either very full or very tight. The men wore their hair either *à la jeune France, à la russe, à la Moyen Âge,* or *à la Titus.* They had smooth chins, mustaches, imperials, sidewhiskers, and even full beards. It would be appropriate, here, to quote Pushkin's line:

What a mixture of faces and dress! [1]

As for the ideas of these people, they were so confused that I won't even try to explain them.

Pechorin was seated diagonally across the table from

---

[1] From "The Robber Brothers," an early poem of Pushkin's.

Princess Ligovskaya. His neighbor on the left was a red-haired gentleman festooned with official decorations, who came to the Pechorins' merely for the dinners. On his right was a woman of thirty, very fresh-complexioned and young-looking, in a crimson beret with feathers, who wore a haughty expression because she passed for a woman of unassailable virtue. From all this we can see that Pechorin, as the host, had chosen the worst place at the table.

Sitting next to Vera was an old lady, dressed up like a doll, with gray eyebrows and wisps of black hair. On her other hand was a diplomat—tall, thin, and pale, with his hair cropped close *à la russe,* who spoke Russian worse than any Frenchman.

After the second course the conversation began to grow lively. "Since you have not been in Petersburg long," the diplomat said to Vera, "you probably have not yet been able to understand and appreciate all the charms of life here. The buildings, which at first glance merely amaze one, as does anything magnificent, will in time become priceless to you, when you recall that our enlightenment has grown and developed in this city. And when you see that it accommodates itself to those buildings easily and pleasantly. Every Russian should love Petersburg. All the best younger men of Russia have come together here, as though on purpose, to extend a friendly hand to Europe. Moscow is only a magnificent monument—the sumptuous and silent grave of the past. But life is here in Petersburg. And our hopes, too, are here."

Such was the lofty eloquence and great wisdom of the tall, thin diplomat, who claimed to be a great patriot.

Princess Ligovskaya smiled and replied rather absently, "Perhaps in time I will come to love Petersburg, too. But we women yield so easily to the habits of the heart—and unfortunately, we think so little about public enlighten-ment and the glory of nations! I love Moscow. My thoughts of Moscow are associated with the memory of such happy days! But here—here everything is so cold, so dead . . . oh, that is not just my own opinion! It is also the opinion of people who live here. They say that once a person has entered the city gates of Petersburg, he changes com-pletely."

As she said these words, she smiled at the diplomat and glanced at Pechorin.

The diplomat grew furious. "What a terrible calumny of our dear city!" he exclaimed. "It is all the fault of that old gossip, Moscow, who slanders her young rival out of envy!"

At the words, 'old gossip,' the fancily-dressed old lady was seized with a violent trembling of the head, and almost choked on her asparagus.

"Princess," the diplomat said, "I suggest that in order to settle our dispute we choose a mediator. Grigory Aleks-androvich, for example. He has been listening to our conversation very attentively. What do you think? Mon-sieur Pechorin, tell us in good conscience, and don't sacri-fice me to the interests of politeness. Princess, do you approve my choice?"

"You have chosen a rather severe judge," she said.

"Be that as it may, we diplomats always pay heed to our own interests," the diplomat replied with a complacent smile. "Monsieur Pechorin, be so kind as to settle the question."

"I'm very sorry," Pechorin said, "but you have made a mistake in your choice. Of your whole argument, I heard only what the princess said."

The diplomat's face dropped. "Nonetheless," he said, "Which do you prefer: Moscow or Petersburg?"

"Moscow is my birthplace," Pechorin answered, trying to get out of it.

But the diplomat insisted stubbornly. "Nonetheless, which—"

"I think," Pechorin interrupted him, "that neither buildings nor enlightenment nor age has any influence on happiness or gay spirits. And the reason people change when they have passed through the city gates of either Petersburg or Moscow is simply that if people didn't change, it would be very boring."

"Princess," the diplomat said, "after a solution like that, I yield my diplomatic title to Monsieur Pechorin. He avoided a definite answer with the skill of a Talleyrand or a Metternich."

She replied, "Grigory Aleksandrovich is not distracted by passion or sympathy. He follows cold reason and nothing else."

"That is true," Pechorin answered. "I have now begun to weigh my words and calculate my acts, following the example of others. Before, when I yielded to my feelings and imagination, people laughed at me and took advantage of my naïveté. But is there anyone who has not done stupid things in his lifetime? And is there anyone who has not regretted it? Today, upon my honor, I am ready to sacrifice the purest and most ethereal love for three thousand serfs plus a distillery and a count's coat-of-arms on my carriage! One must seize the opportunity. Such things don't just fall like manna from heaven—isn't that so?" This unexpected question was addressed to the lady in the crimson beret.

When she heard the unexpected question, the taciturn, virtuous lady woke up, and the ostrich feathers on her beret began to wave. She could not answer right away, because her chaste teeth were chewing a chunk of grouse with the most virtuous vigor. Everyone waited, patiently and in silence, for her answer. Finally she opened her mouth and asked, "Was your question addressed to me?"

"With your kind permission," Pechorin said.

"Do you want to share with me your role of judge and mediator?"

"I should like to pass it on to you entirely."

"Ah, spare me!"

At this moment she was served a course of some kind of rich food. She committed herself to her plate, and then continued. "Why don't you ask the Princess? I'm sure she is a much better judge of love and a count's or prince's title."

"I would like to hear your own opinion," Pechorin said. "And I have resolved to conquer your modesty with stubbornness."

"You are not the first to try, and you will not succeed," she said with a disdainful smile. "Besides, I have no opinion about love."

"Good heavens! At your age you have no opinion about something so important to all women?"

The virtuous lady was insulted. "You mean I'm too old?" she exclaimed, reddening.

"On the contrary, I was about to say that you are still so young—"

"I'm no longer a child, thank God. You did very badly at trying to justify yourself."

"What can I do? I see that I have increased by one more the infinite number of unfortunates who have tried in vain to find favor in your eyes."

She turned away, and he almost laughed out loud. The red-haired gentleman with the decorations asked him in a whisper, "Who is that woman?"

"The Baroness Shtral," Pechorin answered.

"Ah!" the red-haired gentleman exclaimed.

"You have heard a lot about her, naturally?"

"No, nothing explicit."

"She has buried two husbands," Pechorin continued, "and now she's after her third, who will probably outlive her."

"Oho!" the red-haired gentleman said, and continued to gobble up the mushroom sauce.

With this, the conversation came to a halt. But the tall diplomat took upon himself the labor of reviving it. "If you are fond of art," he said to Princess Ligovskaya, "I can tell you a very pleasant piece of news. Bryullov's painting, 'The Last Days of Pompeii,' is coming to Petersburg. Everyone in Italy praised it to the skies, and the French condemned it. Now it will be interesting to see which way the Russian public inclines: toward genuine art, or toward the fashion."

Vera did not answer him. She was preoccupied. To no particular purpose, she had been gazing around at the walls of the dining room; and the word 'painting' only prompted her to fix her attention on a Spanish picture hanging opposite her. It was an old painting, and rather mediocre; but it had acquired value because the colors were faded and the lacquer was cracked. It represented three figures. An old, gray-haired man, seated in an armchair upholstered in velours, had one arm around a young woman. His other hand held a goblet of wine. As he brought his red lips close to the young woman's tender cheek, he was spilling wine on her dress. She, as though submitting reluctantly to his crude caresses, was leaning over the arm of the chair with her elbow resting on his shoulders, but with her head half-averted. Holding a finger to her lips, she was staring fixedly at a half-opened door beyond which two glittering eyes and a knife were gleaming in the darkness.

Vera looked hard at the picture for several minutes, and then asked the diplomat to explain what it meant.

He retrieved his lorgnette from under his cravat, squinted, aimed his lorgnette at the somber canvas from various angles, and then concluded it must be a copy of a Rembrandt or a Murillo. "In any case," he added, "its owner must have a better idea of what it means than I do."

Vera said, "I don't want to trouble Grigory Aleksandrovich to settle any more questions." And again she stared at the picture.

"Its subject is very simple," Pechorin said, without waiting to be asked. "It shows a woman who has abandoned and deceived her lover so that she can more easily deceive a stupid, rich old man. At this moment, apparently, she is wheedling something out of him while she restrains her lover's rage with false promises. When she has got everything she wants out of him by means of sham kisses, she will open the door herself and cold-bloodedly witness a murder."

"Oh! That's frightful!" Vera exclaimed.

Pechorin said, "Perhaps I am mistaken in attributing such a meaning to the picture. My interpretation is quite arbitrary."

"Do you really think such deceit can exist in a woman's heart?"

"Princess," Pechorin answered dryly, "there was a time when I was stupid enough to think I could understand the hearts of women. But recent events in my life have convinced me of the contrary. Therefore, I cannot give a definite answer to your question."

She flushed. The diplomat gave her a searching glance and then began to make doodles on his plate with his fork. The woman in the crimson beret was on pins and needles from hearing such frightful things, and tried to move her chair away from Pechorin's, while the red-haired gentleman smiled meaningfully and swallowed three mushrooms at once. During the rest of the dinner Pechorin and the diplomat were silent. Princess Ligovskaya struck up a conversation with the old woman; the virtuous lady argued heatedly about something or other with her neighbor on the right; and the red-haired gentleman ate.

After the dessert, when the champagne was brought in, Pechorin raised his glass and said to Vera, "Since I was not fortunate enough to be present at your wedding, allow me to congratulate you now."

She looked at him in astonishment and said nothing. Mute suffering was expressed in her mobile features; and her hand, holding a glass of water, began to tremble. Pechorin saw all of this; and something akin to contrition crept into his breast. Why was he torturing her? To what purpose? What good could he derive from this petty vengeance? He could not give himself a precise answer.

Soon there was a scraping of chairs, and everyone got up from the table and went into the reception room. Servants brought coffee on silver trays. Some of the men who did not play whist (Prince Ligovskoy was among them) went into Pechorin's study to smoke their pipes. Vera, on the pretext that her hair needed attention, went to Varenka's room.

She closed the door behind her and flung herself into a big armchair. There was a tightness in her chest from some ineffable emotion. Tears formed on her eyelashes and began to drop faster and faster on her burning cheeks. She cried, bitterly, until it occurred to her that it would be embarrassing to appear in the drawing room with red eyes. She got up and went to the mirror, where she dried her eyes and dabbed her temples with eau de cologne and perfume from the flasks, both crystal and colored, which stood on the dressing table. From time to time a sob would escape her, and her breast would heave. But these things were merely the last waves left behind on the smooth surface of the sea by a hurricane which had passed.

But what was she crying about? you ask. And I in turn ask you if there is anything that women do *not* cry about. For them, tears are a weapon for both offense and defense. Vexation, joy, impotent hatred, and impotent love—for all these things they have one form of expression. Vera Dmitrevna herself could not have said which of these feelings was the chief cause of her tears. She had been deeply hurt by Pechorin's words. But strangely enough she did not conceive any hatred for him because of this. Perhaps if she had been able to detect in his reproach a feeling of regret for the past and a desire to find favor in her eyes again, she might have been able to respond with mordant mockery or a show of indifference. But it seemed that only his vanity was wounded, and not his heart— which is a man's weakest point, like the heel of Achilles; so that in this skirmish he had remained outside the range of her shots. Apparently, Pechorin had haughtily challenged her hatred, in order to see whether it would be as short-lived as her love. And he had achieved his purpose. Her feelings became agitated, and her thoughts confused. The first impression had been strong; and upon that first impression, everything else depended. He knew this; and he also knew that hatred itself is closer to love than indifference.

Vera was on the point of returning to the drawing room when the door suddenly opened with a slight creaking sound, and Varenka came in. "I have been looking for you, *chère amie!*" she exclaimed. "You seem to be ill."

Vera smiled wanly and said, "I have a headache. It's so hot in there."

"I kept looking at you during dinner," Varenka went on. "You weren't talking to anybody. I was sorry I wasn't sitting next to you. Then perhaps you wouldn't have been so bored."

"I wasn't bored in the slightest," Vera answered, smiling rather bitterly. "Grigory Aleksandrovich was very charming."

"Listen to me, my angel. I wish you wouldn't call my brother 'Grigory Aleksandrovich.' It's so formal—as though you two had met only yesterday. Why don't you just call him 'George' in the old way? He's so kind."

"I must say I didn't observe that quality in him just now. He said things to me that another woman would never forgive." Vera was aware that her words had revealed more than she intended. But she reassured herself with the thought that Varenka was a frivolous girl and would either pay no attention to what she had said, or would soon forget it. (To her own misfortune, Vera Dmitrevna was one of those women who are usually more cautious and modest than others, but whose words betray them in moments of strong feeling.)

When she had fixed her hair in front of the mirror, she took Varenka by the arm and they both returned to the drawing room. But we shall go into Pechorin's study, where several of the young men had gathered, and where Prince Ligovskoy, a cigar in his mouth, was vainly trying to get into their conversation. He did not know a single actress in Petersburg; he did not have the key to a single one of the intrigues going on there; and as a visitor from another city he could not tell a single interesting piece of news. Having married a young woman, he tried to appear young in spite of his false teeth and a few wrinkles. At no time during all the years of his youth had this man ever had a passion for anything: women, wine, cards, or honors. Still, he got drunk very often in order to please his comrades and friends; he fell in love two or three times merely to oblige women who were trying to find favor with him; he once gambled away thirty thousand rubles, when it was fashionable to lose; and he ruined his health in the government service because it was agreeable to his superiors. Although an egoist in the highest degree, he was known as a good fellow who was always ready to be of service; and he married because all of his relatives wanted him to do it. Now he was sitting in front of the fireplace, smoking his cigar and finishing his coffee, as he listened closely to the talk of the young men standing across from him. One of them was the artillery officer, Branitsky. Another was a civil servant. The latter was one of the typical figures of Petersburg society.

He was fairly tall, and so thin that his English-tailored frock coat hung from his shoulders as though from a coat-rack. A stiff satin cravat supported his angular chin. His mouth, with virtually no lips, resembled a hole cut in a cardboard mask by a pen-knife; and his hollow, swarthy cheeks were pitted here and there with pockmarks—the after-effects of a severe case of smallpox. His nose was straight, of uniform thickness throughout its length, and looked as though it had been cut off at the end. The eyes, small and gray, had an insolent look. His eyebrows were thick, his forehead high and narrow, and his hair black and close-cropped. A beard *à la Saint-Simonien* peeped out from under his cravat.

He knew everybody; worked somewhere or other; traveled about on special assignments and, when he returned, was promoted. He always frequented the middle stratum of society and talked about his connections with the aristocrats. He chased after rich, marriageable ladies; proposed a great many projects; sold shares in various undertakings; suggested to everybody that they buy various books on subscription; knew all the journalists and men of letters; claimed he was the author of many anonymous articles in the magazines; published a pamphlet that nobody read; was, in his own words, "buried under a heap of work"; and every day spent the entire morning on Nevsky Prospect. By way of completing this character sketch I should add that his last name was Ukrainian, although instead of Gorshenko he called himself Gorshenkov.

"Why don't you ever come to see me?" Branitsky was asking him.

"Believe me, I am *so* busy!" Gorshenko answered. "Tomorrow, for instance, I have to make a personal report to the minister. Then I have to sit on a committee—such a big batch of work I don't know how I'll ever manage it. Besides that, I must write an article for a magazine; and then I have a dinner engagement at the home of Prince X. Every night I attend a ball somewhere. Tonight, for example, at the home of Countess F. So be it. I am already resigned to sacrificing the winter. But next summer I will again lock myself in my study and surround myself with papers. And I will visit nobody except old friends."

Branitsky smiled and walked away, whistling an aria from *Fenella*.

It occurred to Prince Ligovskoy, who had been thinking about his lawsuit, that it would not be a bad idea to become acquainted with a man who knew everybody and made personal reports to the minister. He struck up a conversation with him about politics and the government service, and then about his own business—the lawsuit he was bringing against the Treasury for 54,000 acres of timberland. Finally, he asked Gorshenko whether he knew a certain government employee by the name of Krasinsky in whose section the case was being handled.

"Oh, yes," Gorshenko replied, "I know him. I've seen him often. But he can't do anything. You should get in touch with people who carry weight. I'm familiar with these cases. They have often tried to foist them off on me, but I have always refused."

Prince Ligovskoy was nonplussed by this answer. It seemed to him that an entire committee of ministers stood before him in the person of Gorshenko. "Yes," he said, "in our day these cases have become terribly complicated."

Pechorin, who had heard the conversation and learned from Prince Ligovskoy what department was handling his case, promised to locate Krasinsky and bring him to the Prince. The latter, enraptured by his kindness, shook his hand and invited him to drop in at his home whenever he had some leisure time.

Chapter Seven

The next day Pechorin was on duty. He spent the night in the watch officer's room, and was relieved at noon. By the time he had changed uniform, another hour had passed. When he arrived at the office where the clerk Krasinsky worked, he was told that the latter was out. They gave him Krasinsky's address, and he set out in the direction of the Obukhov Bridge. Stopping in front of a huge building, he called the doorman and asked whether the clerk Krasinsky lived there.

"Please go to Number Forty-Nine," was the answer.

"And how do I get in?"

"From the courtyard."

Number Forty-Nine, and entry from the courtyard! These terrible words cannot be understood by anyone who has not spent at least half of his life trying to locate various government clerks. Forty-nine is a sinister and mysterious number, like 666 in the Apocalypse. First you make your way through a narrow, angular courtyard, in deep snow or mud. High pyramids of firewood threaten at every moment to fall on your head and crush you. A strong odor, acrid and revolting, poisons your breathing. Dogs growl at the sight of you. Pallid faces showing the terrible marks of poverty or debauchery look out from the narrow windows of the ground floor. Finally, after many inquiries, you find the door you are looking for: it is dark and narrow, like the gate of Purgatory. After slipping on the threshold, you skid down two steps and find yourself wading in a puddle formed on the landing of the stone stairs. Then, feeling for the stairs with an unsteady hand, you begin to climb up again. When you reach the second floor and stop on a quadrangular platform, you see several doors around you. But alas! None of them has a number! You start knocking or ringing. Usually a cook comes out with a tallow candle, while from behind her you can hear quarreling or the crying of children.

"What do you want?"

"Number Forty-Nine, please."

"Ain't no such number here."

"Who lives here?"

Usually, she answers with some barbarous name. Or else she says, "What business is it of yours? Try the next floor up!" And she slams the door. The same scene is repeated, with variations, at all of the other doors. The higher up you climb, the worse it gets. A sophist might conclude, from observing this, that the closer man approaches to Heaven, the more he resembles those plants growing on mountain peaks, which lose their color and vitality.

After about an hour of torture, you finally locate Apartment Number Forty-Nine (or some other equally mysterious number); that is, provided the doorman was not drunk and understood your question; provided there are not two clerks with the same name living in the building; provided you did not get the wrong stairway; etc. Pechorin endured all of these tortures and finally, having climbed up to the fourth floor, he knocked on the door. The cook came out, and he asked the usual question, to which she replied, "This is the place." He went in, took off his overcoat in the kitchen, and was about to proceed further when the cook suddenly stopped him, saying that Mr. Krasinsky had not yet come home from the office.

"I will wait," he said, and went on in. The cook followed him, looking him over with astonishment. Apparently, his handsome Guards uniform and white plume were an unusual phenomenon on the fourth floor.

When he entered the drawing room—if this term can be applied to a rectangular room furnished with one table, covered with oilcloth, in front of which stood one old sofa and three chairs—a little old woman of neat appearance got up from her place and repeated the cook's question.

"I am looking for Mr. Krasinsky. Perhaps I have come to the wrong place."

"He is my son," the old lady said. "He'll be home soon."

"If you will allow me to wait—" Pechorin continued.

"Please be so kind," the old lady interrupted, and hastily offered a chair.

Pechorin sat down. As he looked around at the room and its furnishings, he felt rather ill at ease. If fate had suddenly transported him to the palace of the Shah of Persia, he would have felt more at home than here.

At first glance the old lady seemed to be seventy years old, although in fact she was younger. But early sorrows had caused her to become stooped, and had dried up her skin, which had taken on the coloration of old parchment. The bluish veins were clearly visible on her transparent hands; and her face was wrinkled. It was only in her little eyes, apparently, that all of her vital forces were concentrated: they shone with a kind of extraordinary goodwill and imperturbable calm.

At a loss how to begin the conversation, Pechorin started leafing through a book which was lying on the table. He wasn't actually giving any thought to the book, but its title caught his attention: *The Easiest Way to Become Rich and Happy Forever*, by N. P. Moscow; I. Glazunov, printer; 25 kopecks. A smile appeared on Pechorin's face. The book, like a blank lottery ticket, was a vivid representation of disappointed dreams, of unrealistic hopes, of vain efforts to envision a melancholy existence as better than it really was.

The old lady noticed his smile, and said, "I read an advertisement in the newspaper and asked my son to get that book for me, but there's nothing in it."

"I don't think," Pechorin objected, "that any book can teach one how to be happy. Oh, if only happiness were a science! That would be another matter!"

"Of course," the old lady replied, "it is only natural for a drowning man to clutch at a straw. But we weren't always in the situation we are in now. My husband was a Polish nobleman in the service of Russia. As the result of a long lawsuit he lost most of his property; and the rest was plundered during the recent war. But I have my hopes that everything will soon be set right. My son," she continued, with a certain show of pride, "now has a very good position and gets a good salary." After a moment of silence she added: "You have come to see my son on some business, I suppose? Perhaps you will find it tiresome waiting for him. In that case, if you want to tell me what it is, I will inform him."

Pechorin replied, "Prince Ligovskoy wanted me to ask your son whether he would be so kind as to come and see him. The Prince has brought a lawsuit which is to be taken up in Mr. Krasinsky's section. I wish you would give him Prince Ligovskoy's address. And I should be much obliged if you would suggest that your son come tomorrow night. I shall be there myself."

When he had written down the address, Pechorin bowed and went to the door. At that moment the door opened, and he suddenly collided with a man of unusual height. They looked at each other, their eyes met, and each stepped back a pace. Hostile feelings showed in the faces of both men, and they were speechless with astonishment. Finally, in order to get out of this strange situation, Pechorin said almost in a whisper, "Sir, you must remember that I did not know you were Mr. Krasinsky. Otherwise, I should not have had the honor of meeting you here. Your mother will explain to you the purpose of my call."

They moved away from each other without bowing, and Pechorin went out. He was very much disturbed by this trick of fate; because he had recognized Krasinsky as the same clerk he had almost run down a few days before, and with whom he had had words in the theater.

Meantime Krasinsky, no less surprised and upset by the meeting, sat down in an armchair across from his mother, took his head in his hands, and sank deep into thought. When his mother conveyed Pechorin's information to him, trying to explain how profitable it would be to render a service to Prince Ligovskoy, and then began to express her surprise that Pechorin had not explained the matter himself, Krasinsky suddenly jumped up from his chair, his face illuminated by a brilliant idea. He struck the table with his fist and exclaimed, "Yes, I *will* go to see that prince!" Then he started pacing the room, from time to time uttering incoherent ejaculations. The old lady, apparently accustomed to such strange behavior, watched him without surprise. Finally he sat down again, sighed, and looked at his mother as though only waiting for her to start a conversation. She understood.

"*Nu*, Stanislav," she said, "will you be getting your bonus soon? We don't have much money left."

"I don't know," he replied curtly.

"No doubt," she went on, "you haven't managed to please the head of the department. *Nu*, what a pity that you should have to pull the chestnuts out of the fire for him. Your day will come, though. But in the meantime, if you don't learn to please other people, God won't reward you."

Bitterness showed in Stanislav's handsome face, and he answered in a dry voice, "Mother, you want me to sacrifice even my character for you! Well, after all the other sacrifices I have made for you, that would be merely a drop in the bucket!"

She looked up at him with tear-filled eyes, and silence reigned again. Stanislav began to leaf through the book on the table. Suddenly, without taking his eyes from the paragraph in which the anonymous author proves that friendship is the key to true happiness, he asked, "Mother, do you know who that was—that officer who came here today?"

"No, I don't. Why?"

"He is my mortal enemy," Stanislav replied.

The old lady's face paled (to the extent that this was possible) and she clasped her hands and cried, "Mercy on us! What does he want of you?"

"He probably doesn't wish me any evil. But as for me, I have a very good reason for hating him. When he was sitting there across from you with his glittering epaulettes, smoothing his white plume, didn't you feel—couldn't you tell at first glance that I simply must hate him? Believe me, we will meet again on the road of life, and we won't meet as coldly as we did just now. Yes, I will go to see that prince. Some inner premonition tells me I must obey the decrees of fate."

Stanislav's frightened mother made every effort to discover the reason for his deep hatred, but without success: he would not tell her. It was as though he feared that the reason might seem too trifling to her. Like any stubborn and passionate person obsessed by a single fixed idea, more than all other obstacles he strove to avoid the persuasions of reason, which might divert him from his contemplated goal.

The next day he dressed as well as he knew how. Throughout the morning, perhaps for the first time in his life, he carefully studied all of the office dandies, from head to foot, in order to learn how to knot his cravat, and how many buttons on his waistcoat should be buttoned. And he sacrificed twenty-five kopecks to Faguet, the coiffeur, who brutally fluffed his soft curls up into a stiff and awkward top-knot. That evening, when the clock struck seven, Krasinsky set out for Morskaya Street, full of vague hopes and apprehensions.

Chapter Eight

Prince Ligovskoy was playing host to some relatives when Krasinsky entered the vestibule.

"Is the Prince receiving guests?" he asked, looking uncertainly from one lackey to another.

"We don't belong here," one of them answered, not even getting up from his master's fur coat, on which he was lying.

"Well, my good man, can't you call the porter?"

"He will probably come out himself," was the answer. "We mustn't call him."

Finally the porter appeared.

"Is Prince Ligovskoy at home?"

"Yes, sir."

"Tell him that Krasinsky has come. He knows me."

The porter went into the drawing room. Going up to Prince Ligovskoy, he said very quietly, "Mr. Krasinsky is here. He says you know him."

"What Krasinsky? What nonsense are you talking?" the Prince exclaimed, frowning importantly.

Pechorin, who had heard what was going on, hastened

to the aid of the confused porter. "It's that government clerk who is handling your case. I went to see him yesterday."

"Ah! I am much obliged," answered Prince Stepan Stepanych.

He went into his study, having left instructions for the clerk to be directed there.

But rather than listen to their boring talk about the complicated lawsuit, we shall remain in the drawing room. Two old ladies, some sort of chamberlain from the court, and a young man of ordinary appearance were playing whist. Princess Vera and another young woman were sitting on a sofa near the fireplace listening to Pechorin, who had moved his armchair close to the fireplace, where a few embers were still glowing, and was recounting one of his adventures during the Polish campaign. Upon Prince Ligovskoy's leaving the room, Pechorin had taken the master's chair, so as to be closer to Vera.

"And so," said the other young woman (whom Vera called her cousin) by way of resuming the interrupted conversation, "you were ordered to take a platoon and go into the village."

"Naturally, I went," Pechorin said, "although the night was dark and rainy. I had been ordered to relieve the Polish lord of his weapons, if he had any, and send him to headquarters. I had just been made a sublieutenant, and this was my first mission. At dawn we saw, up ahead of us, a peasant village and a stone manor house. On the outskirts of the village my hussars captured a peasant and brought him to me. What he told us about the lord's estate and the number of inhabitants, corresponded to my instructions.

" 'And does your master have a wife or daughters?' I asked.

" 'Yes, Mr. Captain.'

" 'And what is the name of your master Ostrozhky's wife?'

" 'Countess Rozha.'

"She must be a beauty, I thought, wrinkling my brow. 'And are the daughters ugly mugs [1] like their mother?'

" 'No, sir. The big one is called Amalia and the little one Evelina.'

"This still doesn't prove anything, I thought. The idea of Countess Ugly Mug was torturing me, and I continued my interrogation. 'The Countess Rozha herself—is she old?'

" 'No, sir. She is only thirty-three.'

" 'How unfortunate!'

"We entered the village and soon stopped before the gate of the manor house. I told my men to dismount and, accompanied by a noncommissioned officer, went into the house. The whole place was empty. When I had gone through a few rooms, I was met by the count himself, trembling and white as a sheet. I told him what my instructions were. Naturally, he said he had no weapons. He offered me the keys to all of the storerooms, and at

---

[1] A play on the Polish lady's name, Roza, pronounced by the peasant as 'Rozha,' which in Russian means 'ugly mug.'

the same time invited me to take lunch. After the second glass of sherry the count began asking permission to introduce his wife and daughters to me.

" 'For heaven's sake,' I said, 'why all this ceremony?' To tell the truth I was afraid his Rozha would spoil my appetite. But the count insisted. Apparently, he was counting heavily on the strong influence of his Rozha.

"I was still trying to get out of it when suddenly the door opened and a tall, svelte woman in a black dress entered the room. Try to see in your mind's eye a Polish woman—a real Polish beauty—at the very moment when she is attempting to charm a Russian officer. It was the Countess Rozalia herself. Or rather, Roza, which the peasants pronounce 'Rozha.' "

This chance pun seemed very amusing to the two ladies, and they both laughed.

"Something tells me you fell in love with that *Rozha*," the young lady whom Vera called her cousin finally exclaimed.

"It would have happened," Pechorin replied, "except that I already loved another."

"Oho! Constancy!" the young woman said. "Don't you realize that no one boasts of that particular virtue?"

"In me it is not a virtue, but a chronic illness."

"But you have been cured of it, have you not?"

"At least I'm taking treatments," Pechorin replied.

Vera gave him a quick glance. Something like surprise mingled with joy showed on her face. Then suddenly she became sad. This rapid shift of feelings did not escape

Pechorin's attention. He changed the course of the conversation, and the anecdote was left unfinished. Soon it was forgotten in their cheerful and free-flowing talk.

Finally, tea was served, and Prince Ligovskoy came in, followed by Krasinsky. The Prince introduced the latter to his wife, and asked him to have a seat. Everyone in the small group was looking at him closely, and silence reigned. If Prince Ligovskoy had been a Petersburgian, he would have treated Krasinsky to a luncheon costing five hundred rubles. If he had had real need of his services, he would even have invited him to a ball or a noisy rout, to be jostled among other guests of various categories. But not for anything in the world would he have brought into his own drawing room, quite informally, an outsider who in no sense belonged to the upper stratum of society. But the Prince had been brought up in Moscow, and Moscow is such a hospitable old lady!

Out of politeness, Vera directed a few questions at Krasinsky, and he answered briefly and simply. "We are much obliged to Mr. Pechorin," she said, "for having made it possible for us to meet you."

At these words, Pechorin and Krasinsky involuntarily looked at each other, and the latter replied quickly, "I am even more obliged to Mr. Pechorin than you are, for his invaluable good offices."

Pechorin smiled fleetingly—a smile which might have been interpreted to say: "Oho! Our clerk is beginning to pay compliments!" Whether Krasinsky understood this smile, or whether he had frightened himself with his own boldness (because this was probably the first time he had paid a compliment to a woman whose social status was so far above his own), I don't know. But he flushed and continued in an uncertain voice: "Believe me, Princess, I will never forget the pleasant moments you have allowed me to spend in your company. Please have no doubts: I will do everything within my power. Besides, your case merely has to be straightened out. Legally, you are completely in the right . . ."

"Tell me," Vera said, with that degree of interest so much resembling ordinary politeness when one does not know what to say to a stranger—"Tell me: You must be terribly overworked with business matters, aren't you? I can imagine how boring it is: writing and reading long, rambling documents from morning till night. It must be unbearable! Can you believe it? Every day, for a year, now, my husband has been explaining our lawsuit to me. And I haven't yet understood a single thing."

What a kind and considerate husband, Pechorin thought.

"But why should you bother, Princess?" Krasinsky said. "Your portion in life is amusement and elegance; ours is work and worry. And that's the way it should be. If we didn't do the work, who would?"

Finally, this conversation, too, exhausted itself, and Krasinsky rose and took his leave. When he had gone, Vera's cousin remarked that he was by no means so gauche as might have been expected of a clerk, and that in conversation he was not at all stupid. And Vera added: "*Et savez-vous, ma chère, qu'il est très bien.*"

At these words, Pechorin began to exaggerate Krasinsky's cleverness and good looks to the extreme. He averred that he had never seen such handsome dark-and-light blue eyes in any government clerk in the world; and that, to judge from his profound comments, Krasinsky would unquestionably become a great statesman, provided he didn't always remain a titulary councilor. "I must by all means find out," he added very seriously, "whether he has a university diploma."

He succeeded in making the two women laugh, and in changing the topic of conversation. Still, Vera's expression had been deeply engraved in his memory. It seemed to him to have been a reproach—perhaps a chance one, but caustic nonetheless. Before, he himself had admired Krasinsky's nobly handsome face. But when the woman who occupied all of his thoughts and hopes turned her attention to that handsomeness, he understood that she was involuntarily making a comparison which was devastating to him; and it almost seemed that he was again losing her forever. From that moment he began to hate Krasinsky in his own turn. It is a melancholy truth, but one we must recognize, that the purest love is half-mixed with vanity.

Being himself susceptible to external beauty, and possessed of a sharp and penetrating mind, Pechorin was able to look at himself dispassionately. And like most persons whose imagination is very active, he exaggerated his own defects. Since he had learned from his own experience how hard it is to love a person for spiritual qualities alone, he became mistrustful and taught himself to attribute women's attentions or caresses to calculation or mere chance. What another might have taken as proof of the

most tender love, he often dismissed as tokens of decep-
tion, words spoken without real intent, glances and smiles
idly tossed out for whoever wanted to catch them. Another
person would have become dejected and yielded the field
to his rival. But the challenge of the struggle appeals to
a man of stubborn character; and Pechorin made a solemn
pledge to himself that he would be the victor. Following
his system, and arming himself with a *sang-froid* and
patience which were invincible, he could have destroyed
the wily subterfuges of the most artful coquette. He knew
the axiom that sooner or later persons of weak character
must yield to those whose character is strong and unbending, in accordance with some natural law as yet unex-
plained. And it could be said for certain that he would
attain his goal, if only passion—an all-powerful passion—
did not destroy at one blast, like a storm, the high scaffold-
ings of his reasoning and his efforts. But that *if*, that
terrible *if*, almost like the "if" of Archimedes, who promised to raise up the earth if he were provided with a
fulcrum. . . .

Pechorin's mind was besieged by a host of different
thoughts, so that toward the end of the evening he became
preoccupied and said very little. Prince Ligovskoy was
telling a long story dug up from the annals of his family.
The ladies yawned furtively.

"Why have you become so melancholy?" Vera's cousin
finally asked Pechorin.

"I should be ashamed to tell you the reason," he
answered.

"Come, now."

"Envy!"

"Who is it you envy? For example—"

"It couldn't be me, could it?" Prince Ligovskoy said, smiling artfully and failing to grasp the significance of his question. Pechorin immediately conceived the idea that Vera had told her husband of the love that had once been between them, repenting of it as one repents of a childish mistake. If she had, then everything had already been finished between them, and Pechorin, unknown to himself, might unwittingly have been serving as a laughingstock for the husband and wife, or the victim of an insidious plot. I am surprised that this suspicion had not disturbed him before then; but I assure you that it only just occurred to him.

He promised himself that he would find out whether Vera had confessed to her husband. Meantime, he answered: "No, Prince, it is not you—although I could envy you, and everyone should . . . But I admit I would like to have the happy faculty that Krasinsky possesses: the faculty of pleasing everyone at first glance."

"Believe me," Vera said, "a person who pleases quickly, is quickly forgotten."

"Good Lord! Is there anything on this earth that isn't forgotten? And if momentary success is counted as nothing, then where is happiness to be found? Supposing you do find real love, real glory, real wealth. Before you know it, death comes, or sickness, fire, flood, war, peace, rivals, a shift in public opinion—and all your work is for nought! And forgetting? A minute is forgotten just as inexorably as a century is. If I were asked which I wanted—a minute of total bliss or years of ambiguous happiness—I would choose to concentrate all of my feelings and passions on one blissful moment, and then suffer infinitely, rather than to stretch out those feelings and passions little by little, and distribute them numerically in the intervals between boredom and melancholy."

Vera said, "I agree with you completely except for the idea that everything on earth is forgotten. There are things one cannot forget—especially grief."

Her charming face took on an expression which was at once rather cold and rather melancholy; and something resembling a tear glistened as it ran down her long lashes —as a raindrop left on a birch leaf after a storm, moves tremblingly along the leaf's edge until a gust of wind carries it away—God knows where.

Pechorin looked at her in astonishment. But alas! He could in no way explain this strange fit of melancholy. He had parted from her so long ago; and since then he had not known a single detail of her life. It was even very likely that at this moment Vera's feelings had nothing at all to do with him. Who knows how many admirers she may have had after he left for the army? Perhaps one of them had even betrayed her—how could one know?

> Who can explain, who can interpret,
> The ambiguous language of the eyes? [2]

When he got up to take his departure, Vera asked him whether he was going to attend the ball being given two

---

[2] I have not been able to identify these lines (*Kto ob'yasnit, kto rastolkuet/Ochey dvusmyslennyy yazyk . . .*) Perhaps an appeal to the *Sunday Times* is in order.

days later by the Baroness R_____. "I am a bit put out,"
she said, "that the Baroness was so persuasive in her invitation. I know almost no one in society here, and I'm
convinced I shall be bored."

Pechorin replied that he had not yet received an
invitation.

Now I understand, he thought, as he got into his sleigh.
She wants to have someone she knows at the ball, as a
partner. I hope to heaven I'm not invited! No doubt
Liza Negurova will be there . . . Oh, Lord! I seem to
recall that the Negurovs have known Vera for a long time.
But if she dares to . . . At this point his sleigh came to
a halt, and so did his thoughts. When he went into his
study at home, he found on his desk an invitation from
the Baroness.

Chapter Nine

Baroness R_____ was Russian, but she was married to
a baron from Courland—one who had managed in some
way to become terribly rich. She lived on Millionnaya
Street in the very center of the best society. Since eleven
o'clock that night, carriages had been driving up, one
after another, to the brightly lighted entrance of her
house. Along the sidewalk on both sides of the steps a
crowd had assembled—passersby who had stopped out of
curiosity or because they were afraid of being run down
in the street. Among them was Krasinsky. Squeezed against
the wall, he stared enviously at the various important

gentlemen decorated with stars and crosses, whom the lanky footmen were carefully helping out of their carriages, and at the young men who carelessly leaped from their sleighs onto the granite steps. A multitude of thoughts swarmed in his head. How am I inferior to them? he thought. Those faces—pale, exhausted, and distorted by petty passions. Can they really please women who have the right and the possibility of a choice? Money, money, and money alone! What do they care for good looks, intelligence, or a feeling heart? Oh, I will get rich without fail—whatever happens! And then I will force this society to give me my due.

The poor, naïve clerk! He didn't know that for this society one needed not only a handful of gold but also a name embellished by historical associations (of whatever kind)—a name so well known to the servants that the porter would not mispronounce it; a name such that when it was called out some important dowager (judge and lawgiver for the drawing room) would ask, "Who is that? Isn't he related to Prince V____ or Count K____?"

And so, Krasinsky stood near the entrance, huddled up in his overcoat. A carriage drew up, and a woman got out. The diamonds in her hair sparkled in the light from the streetlamps. After her, a man in a bearskin coat stepped down. It was Prince and Princess Ligovskoy. Krasinsky quickly thrust himself forward from the crowd of onlookers and bowed politely, as to an acquaintance. But alas! Either they did not notice him or, which is more likely, they did not recognize him. And indeed, for a woman (who had seen him only once) just about to appear before the formidable court of high society, and a husband following behind his pretty wife as they came to the ball, the crowd of curious onlookers freezing beside the entrance was of no interest. But Krasinsky attributed this extremely simple and casual thing to pride and a deliberate disregard; and at that moment a secret hostility for the Princess was born in his suspicious heart. "Very well," he said to himself as he walked away. "Every dog has his day"—a pathetic proverb of petty hatred.

Meantime, in the ballroom the orchestra was already playing, and the ball began to grow lively. All the best Petersburg society was present. There two ambassadors with their foreign retinues, composed of persons who spoke French very well (which was hardly surprising, by the way) and who therefore aroused great interest on the part of the Russian belles; several generals and government officials; and one English lord, who was traveling for business reasons and therefore didn't deem it necessary either to speak or look about him. On the other hand his spouse, a highborn lady who belonged to the class of the bluestockings and had once been a formidable persecutor of Byron, talked enough for four persons and looked about her with four eyes, if we count the lenses of her lorgnette, which had every bit as much expressiveness as did her eyes themselves. Then there were five or six of our home-grown diplomats who had never traveled at their own expense any further than Revel, and who sharply affirmed that Russia was a completely European nation and that they knew it from one end to the other, since they had been several times to Tsarskoye Selo and

even to Pargolov. From behind their starched cravats they
looked haughtily at the young officers who were apparently enjoying themselves in a most carefree and unre-
strained way. They were convinced that those young men,
laced tightly into their gold-trimmed uniforms, were
capable of nothing more than the mechanical employ-
ments of military service. Also on hand were several
rosy-cheeked youths—young officers with toupees or civil
servants with hair cut *à la russe*—as modest as confidantes
in a classical tragedy, who had recently been presented
to high society by some prominent relative. They had
succeeded in making the acquaintance of only a few of
the ladies, and were afraid that if they asked a stranger
to dance the mazurka or a quadrille, they would encounter
one of those frightful, icy stares that make the heart turn
inside out, like the heart of a patient at the sight of a
dark-colored medicine. So they formed a circle of spec-
tators around the flashing quadrilles, and ate sherbet—
lots and lots of sherbet.

The men who devoted themselves solely to dancing
could be divided into two groups. There were those who
went at it conscientiously, sparing neither their legs nor
their tongues. They danced indefatigably; sat on the edges
of their chairs gazing into the faces of their ladies; smiled;
and threw a significant glance each time a word was
uttered. In short, they performed their duties to perfection. The others—middle-aged men who were ranking,
honored veterans of society—glided casually across the
floor with a dignified bearing and haughty expression,
as though doing it out of charity or consideration for

the hostess. And they spoke only to the lady partner of their vis-à-vis when meeting her in the course of performing a figure.

But oh, the ladies! The ladies were the real adornment of this ball, as of all possible balls. So many sparkling eyes and diamonds! So many rosy lips and rosy ribbons . . . miracles of nature and miracles of the fashion shop . . . Marvelous tiny feet and fabulously small slippers; marble-white shoulders and the best French powder; sonorous phrases borrowed from a fashionable novel; diamonds rented from a jeweler's shop . . . I don't know; but to my way of thinking a woman at a ball constitutes, together with her finery, something integral, indivisible, and altogether special. A woman at a ball is not the same thing as a woman in her own room. Judging a woman's soul and mind after having danced a mazurka with her is the same as judging the opinions and feelings of a journalist after having read one of his articles.

Near the door leading from the ballroom into the drawing room, two over-ripe virgins were seated. They were armed with lorgnettes, and were talking with two or three young men who did not dance. One of the young ladies was Lizaveta Negurova. Her crimson gown lent her pale features somewhat more life than usual; and in general she was tastefully dressed. Counting on this advantage, she responded rather coolly to Pechorin's bow when the latter approached her. (It should be noted, by the way, that when a lady is poorly dressed she is usually much more amiable and accommodating. But of course this does not mean that they should dress badly.) Pechorin

stood near Elizaveta Nikolavna, waiting for her to begin
the conversation, and watched the dancers with an absent
air. Several minutes passed in this way, and she was finally
obliged to tear the seal of silence from her lips. "Why
aren't you dancing?" she asked him.

"At all times and in all places, I follow your example."

"Beginning today, you mean."

"Well, better late than never, isn't that so?"

"Sometimes it is too late."

"Good heavens! What a tragic expression!"

Lizaveta almost took offense. But she tried to smile, and
answered, "For some time, now, I have ceased to be
astonished at your behavior. To others it would seem
very impertinent; but to me it seems very natural. Oh,
I know you very well now!"

"And may one inquire who explained my character to
you so cleverly?"

"Oh, that's a secret," she said, looking at him closely
and putting her fan to her lips.

He leaned over, and with feigned tenderness whispered
into her ear: "Long ago you confided to me one secret
of your heart. Can it be that the other is more important
than the first?"

She reddened, despite her incapacity for blushing. But
it was not out of shame, not because of the memory, and
not out of annoyance. An involuntary feeling of satisfaction, a secret hope of again attracting her inconstant
admirer, of marrying him, or at any rate taking her
revenge—in time, in her own way, as a woman—stirred
briefly in her soul. Women can never forgo such hopes

when there is any possibility of attaining their goal; and they can never forgo such satisfaction when the goal is attained.

Quickly assuming a serious and melancholy look, she said slowly and deliberately, "You are reminding me of things I want to forget."

"But you have not yet forgotten them?" he asked tenderly.

"Please don't go on! I will never believe anything again. You gave me such a lesson . . ."

"I?"

There was more astonishment in that "I?" than in five exclamation points placed in a row. Then Pechorin became thoughtful. "Yes," he said, "I begin to understand now. Someone has slandered me to you. I have so many enemies, and especially, so many friends. Now I understand why, when I went to see you the other day (it was in the morning, and I knew you had visitors) I was not received. Naturally, I will not invite such an insult again."

"But you don't know what the reason was," Elizaveta said quickly. "I had received an anonymous letter in which—"

"In which I was praised and my behavior was interpreted in the best possible light," Pechorin answered, smiling bitterly. "Oh, I can guess who rendered me that service! Still, I beg of you to believe: to believe everything in that letter, just as you have believed it up to this moment."

He began to laugh and made a move as if to leave.

"But if I don't believe it?" Elizaveta exclaimed. She was anxious now.

"There's no use. It is always more profitable to believe the bad rather than the good . . . It's one to twenty that—" He did not finish his sentence. His eyes were fixed on the other door of the ballroom, where there was a small commotion. Elizaveta looked apprehensively in the same direction.

Princess Ligovskaya was walking through the crowd toward the drawing room, with Prince Stepan Stepanych behind her. She was tastefully dressed; only the most severe arbiters of fashion might have noted importantly that she was wearing too many diamonds. She moved slowly through the crowd, which unhurriedly made way for her. Not a single greeting delayed her progress. Glances from a hundred curious eyes, surveying the beautiful stranger from head to foot, caused her tender cheeks to redden. Her eyes were filmed over with a kind of electric [1] moisture; her breast rose and fell unevenly; and one could tell from the expression on her face that her moment of agony had come. She was like an unknown speaker stepping out on the platform for the first time. Her success in the world of society depended upon this ball. One flower out of place, one ribbon badly arranged, would destroy her future forever . . . And indeed, a woman cannot hope for success, she cannot please our dandies, if at first glance people say: *"Elle a l'air bourgeois."* This expression, which has so inappropriately crept into our purely patrician society wields a frightful power over

[1] *Sic* (alas!) But it was very new in 1836.

people's minds, and deprives beauty and charm of all their rights.

Taste, my good sir, the very best of manners, . . .[2]

When Princess Ligovskaya reached the point where Pechorin was standing, she responded to his bow with a slight nod of the head and a quick smile. He wanted to say something, but she turned away. She was looking around the room anxiously, trying to find at least one familiar face. Then she saw Lizaveta Nikolavna. Recognizing each other, the two rivals exchanged greetings very tenderly. At this point someone stepped forward from the crowd of men, and began asking Princess Vera when she had come from Moscow, and so forth. She gradually became more affable, so that one might have bet that if she met ninety-nine acquaintances here, the ninety-ninth would be left with the happy conviction that he had conquered her heart with one glance.

As soon as the Ligovskoys had gone into the drawing room, Lizaveta Nikolavna turned to Pechorin in order to resume their interrupted talk. But he was so pale, so immobile, that she was frightened.

Finally, she said, "That woman's appearance made a very strange impression on you. Have you known her long?"

"Since childhood," Pechorin replied.

---

[2] From Griboyedov's famous "comedy," *Gore ot uma* (variously called, in English, *Woe from Wit, The Trouble with Reason*, etc.) The complete line (from Act II, Sc. 5) reads:

> *Taste, my good sir, the very best of manners—*
> *For everything there is a set of rules.*

"I too used to know her. Whom did she marry?"

Pechorin told her.

"What? Can it really be true that that fellow who was walking behind her so meekly is her husband? If I had met them on the street, I would have taken him for her lackey. I imagine she does whatever she wants with him."

"At any rate, whatever it is possible to do with him."

"And yet she is happy."

"Didn't you see how many diamonds she was wearing?"

"Wealth is not happiness."

"Perhaps not, but it is closer to it than poverty is. There is nothing in such poor taste as to be satisfied with one's lot in a humble cottage with a bowl of buckwheat porridge."

"Who said anything about poverty? In every situation one must know how to choose the middle way."

"I hope you marry a man who shares that opinion."

He walked away. The quadrille had ended, and the orchestra stopped playing. The big ballroom was filled with the sound of voices, high mixed with low, in conversation. There was a shuffling of boots and slippers. Groups began to form. The ladies went into other rooms to get some fresh air and exchange comments. A few of the men followed, not having noticed that they were *de trop*, and that the ladies were trying to get away from them. Princess Ligovskaya came into the ballroom and sat down next to Elizaveta. They renewed their old acquaintanceship, and began a trifling conversation.

A Strange One

A ROMANTIC DRAMA

> *I have decided to dramatize an actual event which has long disturbed me, and which perhaps will not cease to preoccupy me so long as I live.*
>
> *All of my characters are taken from life. I want them to be recognized: then perhaps remorse will touch the souls of such people. But let them not accuse me. I wanted—indeed, I was compelled—to justify the departed soul of the victim.*
>
> *Have I described society accurately? I don't know. In any case it will always remain, for me, an assemblage of unfeeling people, egotistic to the highest degree, and full of envy toward those whose souls have retained even a spark of the celestial fire.*
>
> *And I hand myself over to the judgment of that society.*

Characters [1]

VLADIMIR PAVLOVICH ARBENIN, a young man

PAVEL GRIGOR'YEVICH ("GRIGORICH") ARBENIN, his father

MAR'YA DMITREVNA ARBENINA, his mother

NATAL'YA ("NATASHA") FEDOROVNA ZAGORSKINA, Vladimir's sweetheart

DMITRI VASIL'YEVICH ("VASILICH") BELINSKOY, Vladimir's friend

[1] This list of the *Dramatis Personae* has been provided for the convenience of the reader. There is no such list in the original.

PRINCESS SOPHIA ("SONYUSHKA"), a cousin of Natasha

ANNA NIKOLAYEVNA ("NIKOLAVNA") ZAGORSKINA, Natasha's mother

ANNUSHKA, Mar'ya Dmitrevna's maid

Students RYABINOV   SNEGIN   ZARUTSKOY   VYSHNEVSKOY

A DOCTOR

AN OLD PEASANT

A BUSINESS AGENT (Serf)

TWO OLD LADIES

GUESTS AND SERVANTS

[*The action takes place in Moscow*]

> *The Lady of his love was wed with* **One**
> *Who did not love [her] better . . .*
> *And this the world calls frenzy; but the* **wise**
> *Have a far deeper madness, and the glance*
> *Of melancholy is a fearful gift;*
> *What is it but the telescope of truth?*
> *Which strips the distance of its fantasies,*
> *And brings life near in utter nakedness,*
> *Making the cold reality too real!*
> —LORD BYRON, "The Dream"

Scene I

[*August 26, morning. A room in the home of Pavel Grigoryevich Arbenin. A desk; a bookcase full of books. Pavel Grigorich is sealing a letter.*]

PAVEL GRIGORICH: They say children are a burden for us while they are young, but I think just the opposite is true. A young child must be cared for, taught, and fussed over. But with a boy of twenty it's even worse. You arrange for him to enter the service, and then you tremble every minute for fear he will get into trouble and ruin himself and his good name forever. Frankly, my situation right now is very critical. Vladimir will not enter the military service. First, because as he himself says, he is too headstrong. Second, because he is not good at mathematics. But then, what should he do? Go into the civil service? But all the best positions are already taken. Besides, it's not a good thing . . . bringing up a youngster these days is very difficult. You think, well, now it's all over. Not a bit of it! It's only the beginning!

I'm afraid Vladimir will lose his good name in society, where I have acquired some importance through very hard work. If he does, I will be to blame. They will say, as somebody did the other day, that I haven't brought him up in accordance with his character. But what is character at his age? His chief characteristic is the lack of any character at all. I see now that I have not been strict enough with my son. What good does it do that his thoughts and feelings have developed prematurely? However, I will not give up my plans. I will tell him he must retire from the service after three or four years, and marry a wealthy young woman to improve his finances. Thanks to my gracious spouse, our own finances are completely ruined. I get into a rage every time I remember how she deceived me. Oh treacherous woman! You will bear the full brunt of my vengeance! In poverty, in repentance, and with no hope for the future, you will die far out of my sight! I will never agree to seeing you again. Didn't I do everything she wanted? To dishonor a husband like that! I am very glad that she has no near relatives to help her. (*A pause.*) I believe someone is coming in . . . just as I thought . . .

(*Vladimir Arbenin enters.*)

VLADIMIR: Hello, Father.

PAVEL GRIGORICH: I am very glad you came in just now. We have something to discuss together. It has to do with your future. But you seem rather dejected, my son. Where have you been?

VLADIMIR (*He glances quickly at his father with a sullen expression*): Where have I been, Father?

PAVEL GRIGORICH: What is the meaning of that gloomy look? Is this the way to return a father's affections?

VLADIMIR: Guess where I have been.

PAVEL GRIGORICH: With some scamp like yourself, gambling away your money. Or else you have been to see some beauty who turned you down and made you bitter. What other adventures could upset you? It looks as though I guessed right.

VLADIMIR: I have been to a place far removed from any gaiety. I have been to see a certain woman, weak and sick, who was abandoned by her husband and relatives for something she did long ago. She is almost destitute. The whole world laughs at her, and nobody takes pity on her . . . Oh, Father! She deserved forgiveness and a better fate! Father! I saw her bitter tears of remorse. I prayed with her. I threw my arms around her knees. I . . . I have been to see my mother. What else do you want to know?

PAVEL GRIGORICH: *You?*

VLADIMIR: Oh, if you knew . . . if you had seen . . . Father, you did not understand that tender, divine soul. Or else you were unjust . . . Yes, unjust! I will repeat it before the whole world—in a voice so loud that the angels will hear, and be horrified at the cruelty of humans.

PAVEL GRIGORICH: (*his face livid*): You dare! You dare to accuse me, you ungrateful—

VLADIMIR: You must forgive me. I forgot what I was saying. But judge for yourself: How could I remain indifferent? No doubt she offended you—offended you inexcusably. But what did she do to me? I spent the first years of my childhood in her lap. Her name, and yours, were the first words I spoke. My first illnesses were eased by her caresses. And now that she has come here to Moscow, poverty-stricken, how could I do anything else but fall at her feet? . . . She wants to see you, Father. I beg you . . . If my happiness means anything to you . . . A single one of her pure tears would wipe out your prejudices and the black suspicion in your heart!

PAVEL GRIGORICH: Listen, you impudent boy! I am not angry with her. But I don't want to see her again. And I mustn't. What would people say?

VLADIMIR (*biting his lips*): What would people say!

PAVEL GRIGORICH: Moreover, my son, it was very wrong of you not to tell me that you were going to see Mar'ya Dmitrevna. I would have given you a warning—

VLADIMIR: A warning that would have killed her last hopes, isn't that right?

PAVEL GRIGORICH: Yes! She hasn't been punished enough yet. That strumpet! That evil woman!

VLADIMIR: She is my mother.

PAVEL GRIGORICH: If you see her again, you can advise her not to come to me, and not to ask forgiveness, so that we can avoid a meeting which would be even more shameful than our parting was.

VLADIMIR: Father! I am not the kind who can carry out an order like that.

PAVEL GRIGORICH (*with a cold smile*): Enough of this! It is not for you to judge which of us is right or guilty. Come to see me in my study an hour from now, and I will show you some papers which concern you. I will let you read a letter from a count relating to an appointment in the civil service. And once more I must ask you not to mention your mother to me again. I ask you, when I could order you!

(*He leaves the room. For some time, Vladimir stares at the door through which his father has left.*)

VLADIMIR: How pleased he is that he has the right to give me orders! Oh dear God! Never before have I bothered You with needless prayers. But now I beg of You: Put an end to this quarrel! . . . I find human beings absurd. They quarrel over nothing, and then put off the hour of reconciliation, as though it were something that could always be managed easily. No, I see now that one must be harsh in order to live with human beings. They think I was created merely to gratify their whims—that I am a means for achieving their stupid ends. Nobody understands me. Nobody knows how to deal with my heart, which is full of love that must be squandered uselessly.

(*Enter Belinskoy, dressed in his best clothes.*)

BELINSKOY: Ah! Greetings, my good friend! Why so pensive? Why count the stars when you can count hard cash? Look at me. I'll bet I can guess what you are thinking about.

VLADIMIR: Shake on it! (*He shakes Belinskoy's hand.*)

BELINSKOY: You were thinking of how to make a woman love you. Or else how to make her admit she was only pretending. Either one is very hard to do. But I would rather try the former than the latter, because—

VLADIMIR: What are you going on about?

BELINSKOY: What about? Either you've become stupid, or you've lost your hearing. I was talking about King Solomon, who preached moderation and advised people to abstain from the fleshpots, although he himself was hardly among the last when it came to partaking. Ha, ha, ha! You no doubt expected that your charming lady would fly to you on the wings of the zephyr. But you're wrong. You yourself should try to fly. Oh, my friend! Is there anybody who can understand women? At the very moment when you think—

VLADIMIR (*interrupting him*): Where were you yesterday?

BELINSKOY: At a musical soiree, so to speak. The children were giving a surprise party for their father on his name day. They played on various instruments. For the father and them, it was fine. But for the guests, of which there were many, it was terribly boring.

VLADIMIR: Ridiculous people! Family pleasures are always spoiled by that kind of stupid conceit!

BELINSKOY: The father was in raptures. He kept looking at everybody in turn, fidgeting in his chair. The guests would respond with a shake of the head and a smile of contentment. Then, when the father had looked the other way, they would yawn pitilessly . . .

VLADIMIR: To me, such shameless guests are miserable creatures. I cannot look on indifferently while someone is expressing contempt for the happiness of another, regardless of what kind it is. Everybody wants others to be happy according to *his* way of thinking. And so they cut the heart to the quick, without being able to heal it. I would like to get completely away from people; but habit won't let me do it. When I'm alone it seems to me that nobody loves me or cares about me. And it's so hard to bear— so hard!

BELINSKOY: Come now, friend! Don't talk any more of that nonsense. All your friends like you. And if there are a few unpleasant things, you must learn to bear up with firmness. Everything passes away, both the good and the bad.

VLADIMIR: Bear up! Bear up! How long have they been preaching that to the human race! And yet they know that almost nobody follows such advice.

Once I too was happy and innocent. But those days are too far gone in the past for their memory to give me any consolation. All of my real life consists of a few moments. And all the rest of time was either merely a preparation for those moments, or their consequences . . . It is hard for you to understand my dreams—I can see that, my friend. Where shall I find the thing I am compelled to seek?

BELINSKOY: In your heart. You possess a great wellspring of happiness. All you have to do is learn to draw upon it. You have the nasty habit of looking at things from all angles—of anatomizing each bit of grief that fate sends you. Learn how to disdain troublesome things, to enjoy the present, to have no concern for the future, and no regrets about the past. With human beings, everything is habit; and with you it is even more that way than with others. Why not stop, if you see that the goal cannot be reached? But no! You must have it then and there! And afterward, who is it that suffers?

VLADIMIR: Don't take such a superficial view of things. Instead, try to put yourself in my place. Do you know, I sometimes envy orphans. Sometimes it seems to me that my parents are quarreling over my love. And then again it seems that they don't value it at all. They know that I love them as much as a son can. Oh, why? Why, when they are glaring at each other, does there exist a being who wants to reunite them—to put all the flame of his young love into their prejudiced hearts? Dmitri, my friend! I shouldn't talk like this. But then you know everything there is to know. To you I can confide the things that make my life a miserable one—the things that will soon lead me to the grave, or to madness.

BELINSKOY: Mohammed said that he put his head into the water and took it out again, and in that interval of time he grew older by fourteen years. In the same way, you have changed frightfully in a very short time. But tell me: How is your love life getting on? You are frowning! What's the matter? Haven't you seen her for a long time?

VLADIMIR: No.

BELINSKOY: And where do the Zagorskins live? There are two sisters, and the father is dead, isn't that right?

VLADIMIR: Right.

BELINSKOY: Introduce me to them. Do they have soirees or give balls?

VLADIMIR: No.

BELINSKOY: But I thought . . . However, it still doesn't matter. Introduce me.

VLADIMIR: If you wish.

BELINSKOY: Tell me the story of your love.

VLADIMIR: It is very ordinary, and wouldn't interest you.

BELINSKOY: Do you know the Zagorskins' cousin— the young princess? She is a very pretty and charming girl.

VLADIMIR: That may be. The first time I saw her I felt a kind of antipathy. I had a bad opinion of her without even having heard a word about her. And you know that I believe in premonitions.

BELINSKOY: Superstition!

VLADIMIR: The other day I was out horseback riding, and my horse did not want to go through a certain gate. I spurred him on. He shied, and I almost hit my head against the gatepost. It's the same way with your soul. Sometimes you feel a dislike toward somebody, and you make an effort to treat him gently—you try to like him. And then, before you know it, he has repaid you with trickery and ingratitude.

BELINSKOY (*looking at his watch*): Good Lord! I should have left long ago! I only dropped in to see you for a minute.

VLADIMIR: I can see that. Where are you rushing off to?

BELINSKOY: To Count Pronsky's. It will be a deadly bore, but I have to go.

VLADIMIR: Why do you have to?

BELINSKOY: Well, just because.

VLADIMIR: A very good reason. Well, good-bye.

BELINSKOY: Good-bye. (*He leaves.*)

VLADIMIR: I like Belinskoy for his cheerful nature. (*He walks back and forth.*) My head is in a whirl. It's all helter-skelter inside, like a house where the master is drunk.

I'll go . . . I'll go and see Natasha, that angel! A woman's glance, like a ray of moonlight, brings peace to my breast. (*He sits down and takes a piece of paper from his pocket.*) Yesterday I found this among my papers, and I was astounded. Every time I look at this slip of paper, I feel the presence of a supernatural power; and a mysterious voice whispers to me: "Don't try to avoid your fate! This is the way it must be!" A year ago, when I saw her for the first time, I jotted down one comment about her. At that time she had a beneficent influence on me. But now—now, when I remember, the blood races in my veins. And I ask myself regretfully why I am not as good—why my soul is not so pure—as I would like. It may be that she loves me: her eyes, her blushes, her words . . . What a child I am! All those things are as clear in my memory, and as precious, as though my life depended upon nothing but her glances and words. But what's the use? The end that I anticipated last year is coming. Great God! What does my heart require? When I am away from her, I imagine what I will say to her, how warmly I will squeeze her hand, how I will recall the past—all the details. But when I am with her, I forget everything. I'm like a graven image. My soul drowns in her eyes, and everything else fades away—hopes, fears, and memories. Oh, what a worthless person I am! I can't even tell her that I love her—that she is more precious to me than life itself. I can't say anything that makes sense when I am sitting next to that marvelous creature! (*He smiles bitterly*). However my life may end, it began rather well. Besides, does it make any difference what kind of memories I take with me to the grave? Oh, how I would like to give myself over to pleasures and let them engulf the heavy burden of self-knowledge that has been my lot since childhood! (*He leaves quietly.*)

Scene II

[*August 28; toward evening. The sitting room at the Zagorskins. One open door leads into the drawing room, the other into the reception hall. Anna Nikolayevna Zagorskina, the hostess; her daughter, Natasha Fedorovna*

*Zagorskina. Presently, Princess Sophia. Some of the guests
are seated, others are standing as they chat. The clock
strikes eight*].

ANNA NIKOLAVNA (*to one of her guests*): Were you at
the Count's yesterday evening? I understand they put on
an amateur theatrical production there. People are still
talking about how the rooms were decorated. It was marvelous . . . majestic, they say.

FIRST GUEST: Yes, of course I was there. They danced
until five in the morning. I had more than my fill of
everything, including all kinds of people . . .

NATASHA: You are such scoffers! And what young men
were there?

FIRST GUEST: The two princes Shumov, Belinskoy, Arbenin, Slenov, Chatsky . . . and others. Some I don't
remember; others I have forgotten . . . Do you know
Belinskoy? A very likeable lad—most charming, isn't that
so?

ANNA NIKOLAVKA: Yes, so I've heard.

ONE OF THE YOUNG LADIES: Tell me, please. What is that
Arbenin like? I've heard a lot about him.

FIRST GUEST: In the first place, he is terribly wild: a
scoffer, and one with a malicious tongue. He is impudent,
and everything else you can think of. Incidentally, he's
very intelligent. Don't think that I am saying this for
personal reasons. Everyone else has the same opinion of
him.

NATASHA: Not everyone, I assure you. I, for one, do
not have that opinion of him. I have known him for a
long time. He comes to see us, and I have not noticed

that he is malicious. At any rate, he never talked to me about anyone the way you talked about him just now . . .

FIRST GUEST: Oh, that's something else again! With you he may be very charming, but—

ANOTHER YOUNG LADY: I also heard that Arbenin is someone to be feared.

SECOND GUEST (*joining them*): It seems to me, on the contrary—

NATASHA (*to one of the young ladies*): *Ma chère,* do you know anything more stupid than compliments?

THIRD GUEST (*who has just come up*): Do you know Arbenin's life story?

ONE OF THE LADIES: I didn't think he was important enough for his life story to be interesting. And what does it matter, anyway? He is very happy—you can tell that from his lighthearted disposition. And the life stories of happy people are never interesting.

THIRD GUEST: Believe me, gaiety among others is often only a mask. But there are moments when that very gaiety, struggling against inner grief, takes on the look of something savage. If sudden laughter puts an end to gloomy pensiveness, it is not joy that prompts such a laugh. This kind of sudden change only shows that a person cannot completely hide his feelings. The faces that are always smiling—those are the faces of happy people!

NATASHA: Oh, I know you always come to the defense of Arbenin!

THIRD GUEST: Don't you ever come to the defense of people who are being unjustly accused?

NATASHA: On the contrary! Just two days ago I quarreled with my uncle, who said Arbenin didn't deserve the title of a nobleman. That he had a malicious tongue, and so on . . . But I know that Arbenin understands honor better than anyone else, and that he has a good heart. He has demonstrated that in many ways.

FIRST GUEST (*turning to another guest*): Just look at her! Isn't she a beauty?

FOURTH GUEST: *C'est une coquette!*

NATASHA (*looking toward the door*): Who is coming now? Oh, just imagine! I didn't recognize my cousin from here!

(PRINCESS SOPHIA *enters. The cousins embrace.*)

SOPHIA (*in a low voice, to Natasha*): Just now, when I was getting out of my carriage, I saw Arbenin. He was walking past the house and staring at the windows so hard that if the Emperor himself had passed on the other side, he wouldn't have turned around. (*She smiles.*) Will he be here?

NATASHA: How should I know? I didn't ask, and he never tells us in advance when he is coming.

SOPHIA (*aside*): And I was hoping to see him again! (*Aloud*) I have something of a headache today.

SECOND GUEST: Just so it isn't your heart!

SOPHIA (*aside*): How trite! (*to him*) Yesterday evening, at the Count's, you performed your part beautifully— especially in the second skit. Everyone was delighted. (*He bows.*) But tell me: Why did you leave so early—right after dinner?

SECOND GUEST: I had a headache.

SOPHIA (*smiling*): What did it matter? It wasn't your heart.

ANNA NIKOLAVNA (*joining them*): Ladies and gentle-men, wouldn't you like to play cards? The tables are ready.

VARIOUS VOICES: With pleasure.

(*All but Natasha and Sophia leave the room.*)

SOPHIA: Cousin, it doesn't look to me as though you were enjoying your victory. You don't seem to understand what I mean. But why be coy about it? Everyone has noticed that Arbenin is in love with you—and you noticed it first of all. Why are you so reluctant to confide in me? You know we have always been close, and I have always told you everything about myself. Or perhaps I have not yet deserved—

NATASHA: *Dushenka!* Why these reproaches? (*Kisses her.*) Besides, that's not true! (*Takes Sophia by the hand.*) Just don't be angry with me, Sophia Nikolovna! (*She smiles.*)

SOPHIA: Oh, I know you like him. But be careful. You don't know Arbenin well, because no one can know him well . . . He has ideas that are caustic and yet profound; desires that know no limit; and inclinations that change from one moment to the next. Those are the things that make your nice young man dangerous. He himself doesn't know what he wants. And for that reason, when he has fallen in love, he will immediately fall out of love again if he sees a new object to pursue.

NATASHA: You seem very wrought up about it, cousin.

SOPHIA: Because I love you and want to warn you.

NATASHA: But how do you happen to know him so well?

SOPHIA: Oh, I have heard plenty.

NATASHA: From whom?

SOPHIA: From Arbenin himself. (*Natasha turns and walks off a way.*) She is jealous! She loves him! And he . . . How often, when I was telling him something, he would sit and stare, not listening to me, as though one single thought occupied his whole being. And when Natasha came in, I would watch his face—and his eyes would suddenly sparkle! Oh, how unhappy I am! But how can I help loving him? He is so intelligent, so full of nobility. He often talks to me, but it's almost always about Natasha. I know he enjoys being with me; but I also know that it's not because of me. And so the thing that should be an inexhaustible source of happiness for me is transformed, by that one thought, into torture.

He is not handsome. But he is so unlike other people that even his defects are somehow pleasing, like something rare. What soulfulness shines in his dark eyes! And his voice . . . Oh, I am mad! I rack my brains over his character, and can't understand my own passion. (*After a pause*) No! They shall not be happy! I swear by Heaven, by my soul, that I will use every poisonous means of female cunning to destroy their happiness . . . And if I too am destroyed, it won't matter. I'll be consoled when I tell myself: "Though I may be crying, he isn't happy either. His life is no more tranquil than my own!" I have decided. How much better I feel! I have decided!

(*During this time several guests have been coming and going backstage: some leaving, others arriving. The hostess has been saying her good-byes to the former and welcoming the latter. Vladimir Arbenin quietly enters from the drawing room.*)

SOPHIA *(noticing Arbenin)* : How did I find the courage to decide?

VLADIMIR: Ah, Princess! How glad I am that you are here!

SOPHIA: Have you been here long?

VLADIMIR: I just arrived. I went into the drawing room: they had the card tables set up and were playing 100 for stakes of five kopecks. I watched them, and hardly said a word. It was oppressive. I don't understand why people play those stupid card games. There is no pleasure for the eyes, and none for the mind. There is not even the hope— so enticing for many people—of winning, or emptying the pockets of your opponent. Half the young people of Russia are dominated by an insufferable kind of grubbiness, a petty exhibitionism, striving toward nothingness. They wander around aimlessly, boring themselves and others.

SOPHIA: Why did you come, then?

VLADIMIR: *(shrugging his shoulders)* : Why, indeed?

SOPHIA *(caustically)*: I can guess!

VLADIMIR: That's right: illusion! Illusion! But tell me: Can a person be happy when his own presence is a burden to others? I was not made for the people of this century and this country. With them, every individual has to sacrifice his feelings and thoughts to the crowd. But I can't do it. Everywhere I go, I am alone. And so I don't belong anywhere. This is a very clear proof, isn't it?

SOPHIA: You are very hard on yourself.

VLADIMIR: Yes, I am my own enemy, because I'm willing to sell my soul for one tender look—for one word that is not altogether cold. My madness is reaching an extreme point. I am going to suffer woe—not from wit, but from stupidity . . .

SOPHIA: Why all these affected gloomy premonitions? I don't understand you. Everything will pass away. Both your woes and your . . . I don't know what to call them . . . your chimeras will disappear. Let's go on in and play cards. Have you seen my cousin, Natasha?

VLADIMIR: When I came in she was talking to some aide-de-camp who was fluttering his epaulets. He was telling her how, at a masquerade he went to recently, a man let his dancing partner fall to the floor. Her husband, coming to the lady's rescue, felt very foolish when he found out who she was. Your cousin laughed uproariously, and that delighted me. Just watch how gay I shall be now! (*He goes into the drawing room.*)

SOPHIA (*watching him go*): I wish you every success! Now I'll begin putting my plan into action, and soon it will all be over . . . Heavens! Why am I so irresolute . . . so weak-willed? (*She goes into the drawing room.*)

Scene III

[*September 15; morning. A room in the home of Mar'ya Dmitrevna Arbenina, Vladimir's mother. A table and an armchair; green wallpaper. Annushka, an old servant woman, is seated near the window, sewing. Sound of wind and rain.*]

ANNUSHKA: The wind and rain are knocking at our windows like travelers who have lost their way. Somebody should say to them: "Wind and rain, go away! There's lots of rich people here. Go and bother them, and keep them from sleeping. We get precious little sleep and quiet as it is.

My mistress came here to make peace with her husband. Oh, oh, oh! It didn't begin peacefully, and it isn't going to end that way. He is letting us almost starve to death. That means he doesn't love her, and never did. If that's so, there won't be any peacemaking. Better no husband at all than a bad husband. Why does Mar'ya Dmitrevna still love that Antichrist? Well, once some people have made up their minds, there's no stopping them.

But then the young master turned out well. Such a sweet one! It's six years now . . . no, more than that . . . eight years since I haw him the last time. How he has grown up! How much better he looks! I still remember how I used to hold him. Such a curiosity he had! Anything he saw, he was always asking, "Why? What for?" And hot-tempered, he was, like gunpowder. Once he took it into his head to throw the plates and glasses on the floor. In a rage, he was, and began to cry, "Throw on the floor!" I gave him the dishes. He threw everything on the floor, and then quieted down . . . And I remember . . . he was three then . . . I remember how the mistress would put him on her lap and begin to play something sad on the piano. Before you knew it the little one's face would be all wet from his tears.

It's likely Pavel Grigorich has told him lots of things to set him against his mother. But you can see he didn't gain anything by it. May God give good health to Vladimir

Pavlovich! He doesn't forget me in my old age. He gives me something, even if it's only sweet words.

(*Mar'ya Dmitrevna comes in, carrying a book.*)

MAR'YA DMITREVNA: I wanted to read something. But how can a person read with his eyes only, when his thought isn't following the words? A miserable state to be in! The incomprehensible will of fate! The frightful struggle of feminine pride against necessity!

What was the use of my childhood dreams? What good does it do to have such vain premonitions? When I was a little girl, under the influence of the clear sky, the bright sun, and joyous nature, I often imagined the kind of beings that my heart demanded. They followed me everywhere. I talked with them day and night. They made the whole world beautiful for me. Even real people seemed better to me, because in some ways they resembled my ideals. From being with them, I myself became better. Were they angels? I don't know. But they were very much like angels. And now a cold reality has deprived me of my last consolation: my ability to imagine happiness!

Since I have neither relatives nor money of my own, I must degrade myself in order to obtain forgiveness from my husband. Forgiveness? That I should seek forgiveness! Dear God! You know human affairs. You have read in my soul and his; and You have seen in which one the cause of all the evil lay! (*She grows thoughtful; then comes to the armchair and sits down.*) Annushka! Did you go to Pavel Grigorich's today, as I told you to, and find out how things stood? All of the old servants there like you. Well, what did you find out about my son?

ANNUSHKA: I went, *matushka,* and I asked.

MAR'YA DMITREVNA: Yes? And what has Pavel Grigorich been saying about me? Didn't you find out?

ANNUSHKA: He hasn't been saying anything about you, *sudarynya.* If you didn't have a son, nobody would know that Pavel Grigorich was married.

MAR'YA DMITREVNA: Not a word about me? He is ashamed to say my name! He has only contempt for me! Contempt! How close it is to sympathy! How close these two feelings are to each other—like life and death.

ANNUSHKA: But they say that Vladimir Pavlovich loves you very much. It is easy to see that when his father tried to blacken your name, it didn't work.

MAR'YA DMITREVNA: Yes, my son loves me! I saw that yesterday. I felt the warmth of his hand, I felt that he is still mine. It's true—the soul does not change. He is just the same as when he used to sit on my lap, those evenings when I was still happy, before frailty—nothing but frailty —had set both Heaven and man against me! (*She covers her face with her hands.*)

ANNUSHKA: Eh, *matushka!* Why cry over the past, when you don't have tears enough for the present? They say that Pavel Grigorish scolded the young master—gave him a really fierce scolding—because he came to see you. And he told him, I guess, that he couldn't come to see us again.

MAR'YA DMITREVNA: Oh! That's impossible! It's too cruel! Not to let a son see his mother when she is weak, sick, and poor—when she is living just a few steps away. Oh, no! That is against nature! Annushka, did he really say that?

ANNUSHKA: Really, *sudarynya.*

MAR'YA DMITREVNA: And he forbade my son to see me? Really?

ANNUSHKA: Yes, ma'am, he did.

MAR'YA DMITREVNA (*after a moment of silence*): Listen to me. He thinks that Vladimir is not his son. Or else he himself never knew his own mother! (*The wind blows even harder against the windowpanes. Both women shiver.*) And I came to make peace! With what kind of a man? No! Reunion with him means rupture with Heaven. I know my husband is an instrument of the divine wrath. But dear God! Would You use a virtuous person as an instrument of punishment? Do honorable people act as hangmen on this earth?

ANNUSHKA: How pale you are, *sudarynya!* Wouldn't you like to rest? (*She looks at the clock.*) The doctor will come soon. He promised to be here at twelve o'clock.

MAR'YA DMITREVNA: And he is coming for the last time. How absurd I look, even to myself. The idea that a doctor can cure a deep wound of the heart! (*After a pause*) Oh, why didn't I take advantage of the thousand-and-one opportunities for reconciliation while there was still time? But now, when my sleep is over, I look for dreams! It is too late, too late! To feel and understand that it is in vain—that's what is killing me. Oh, repentance! Why do you gnaw at my soul because of one momentary deed. What degradation! I had to come to Moscow under another name, so as not to make my son blush before the world. Before the world? But the world today is a collection of fools and evildoers. They forgive nothing, as if they themselves were saints.

ANNUSHKA (*looking out the window*): The doctor has come.

(*The Doctor enters.*)

MAR'YA DMITREVNA: How do you do, Khristofor Vasil'ich. Please come in.

DOCTOR (*approaching and taking her hand*): How are you feeling?

MAR'YA DMITREVNA: Thanks to you, I'm much better.

DOCTOR (*feeling her pulse*): On the contrary! On the contrary! You are weaker. The bile has affected the blood and caused a disturbance. Your nerves are terribly frayed. I told you, remember, that you should be treated for a long time, gradually, according to the right method. But you want to do it all at once.

MAR'YA DMITREVNA: But if the funds are not available?

DOCTOR: Ah, Madame! Your health is your most precious possession! (*He writes out a prescription.*)

MAR'YA DMITREVNA: Where have you come from just now, Doctor?

DOCTOR: From Arbenin's.

MAR'YA DMITREVNA and ANNUSHKA (*together*): *From Arbenin's?* (*Both are confused.*)

DOCTOR: Do you happen to know him?

MAR'YA DMITREVNA: No. What Arbenin?

DOCTOR: The Arbenin who is a collegiate assessor—the one who is divorced from his wife. Or rather, he isn't divorced. His wife left him because she had been unfaithful.

MAR'YA DMITREVNA: Unfaithful? *She* left *him?*

DOCTOR: Yes, unfaithful. They say she had an affair

with some Frenchman. That same Arbenin has a son—a young man of nineteen or twenty. A wild one, a rake, who has acquired a very bad reputation. They say he even drinks. Yes, that's what they say! Why are you staring at me? Everybody feels sorry that such a respected man as Arbenin—a man so well known in Moscow—should have such a worthless son. He is received in good society, but only because of his father. Not only that, but if you can imagine it, they say he makes sport of me and my professional skill. To think that he makes sport of my professional skill!

MAR'YA DMITREVNA (*aside*): Personal remarks! (*Aloud*) I'm going to take a rest.

DOCTOR: Aha! There are red spots on your face. I told you that you were not entirely well yet.

MAR'YA DMITREVNA: They will go away, Doctor. Thank you for the news. And allow you me to bid you farewell. You have a very good idea of the position I am in. I shall soon be leaving Moscow. Since I am without funds, I must return to the country.

DOCTOR: What? Without having recovered your health?

MAR'YA DMITREVNA: I know now that the doctors can't return it to me. My illness is not within their competence.

DOCTOR: What? You don't believe in the beneficial effect of medicine?

MAR'YA DMITREVNA: I beg your pardon! I believe in it very firmly . . . However, I cannot take advantage of it.

DOCTOR: Nothing is impossible for a person of strong will.

MAR'YA DMITREVNA: It is my duty, my will, to go to the

country. At my country home, thirty families of peasants live much more tranquilly than counts and princes. There, in the solitude and the fresh air, my health will return to me. And it is there that I want to die. I no longer require your visits. Thank you for everything. And allow me to give you a final token of my gratitude.

DOCTOR (*taking the money*): But you are still very sick. You should—

MAR'YA DMITREVNA (*giving him a meaningful look*): Good-bye!

(*The Doctor bows and leaves, with an expression of dissatisfaction.*)

That man would squeeze the last kopeck out of you!

ANNUSHKA: You are all upset—your face has changed. *Akh, sudarynya!* You must sit down. Your hands are shaking.

MAR'YA DMITREVNA: My son is meeting with the same fate as myself.

ANNUSHKA (*supporting her*): It looks, ma'am, as though you were just cut out to suffer.

MAR'YA DMITREVNA: I want to die.

ANNUSHKA: Death takes all of us sooner or later. Why ask him to come? He knows when he's supposed to take us . . . But if you call him at the wrong time, things will be even worse. Pray to God, *sudarynya!* And to the holy saints. To be sure, they've all suffered no less than us. And such sufferings they were, *matushka!*

MAR'YA DMITREVNA: I see my end is near. Such premonitions have never failed me. Oh God! Grant only that I may make peace with my husband before I die! I want

no one's just reproach following me to the grave. Annushka, take me to my room.

Scene IV

[*October 17; evening. The room of the student, Ryabinov.
Bottles of champagne on the table, and considerable disorder. Snegin, Chelyaev, Ryabinov, Zarutskoy, and Vyshnevskoy are smoking their pipes. None of them is over
twenty years old.*]

SNEGIN: What happened to him? Why did he jump up
and run out without saying a word?

CHELYAEV: He took offense at something or other.

ZARUTSKOY: I don't think so. He's always like that. One
moment he's joking and laughing; the next moment he
stops talking and turns into a stump. Then suddenly he
jumps up and runs out as though the ceiling were falling
in on him.

SNEGIN: To the health of Arbenin! *Sacré Dieu!* He's a
wonderful friend!

RYABINOV: A toast!

VYSHNEVSKOY: Chelyaev, did you go to the theater last
night?

CHELYAEV: Yes, I did.

VYSHNEVSKOY: What did you see?

CHELYAEV: Schiller's *Robbers,* in a version like a plucked
chicken. Mochalov [2] was terribly lackadaisical. It's too bad
that fine actor is not always at his best. It might have hap-

---

2 P. S. Mochalov (1800–48), considered a fine tragic actor, was nonetheless uneven in his performances.

pened that I was seeing him for the first and last time. That's the way he hurts his reputation.

VYSHNEVSKOY: And no doubt you were scared to death in the theater?

CHELYAEV: Scared? Of what?

VYSHNEVSKOY: Why? Because you were alone with the robbers.

ALL: Bravo; *Fuora!* A toast!

SNEGIN (*He takes Zarutskoy to one side*): Is it true that Arbenin writes?

ZARUTSKOY: Yes: and rather well, too.

SNEGIN: I see. Could you get something of his for me?

ZARUTSKOY: Of course. I have some with me right now.

SNEGIN: Please show them to me. Let the rest of them go on with their drinking and horseplay. We'll sit down here, and you can read them to me.

(*They sit down near the window in the other room, and Zarutskoy takes a few slips of paper from his pocket.*)

ZARUTSKOY: Here is the first one. It is a fragment—a bit of fantasy. Listen closely . . . Good Lord! What a lot of noise they're making! By the way, I should tell you that Arbenin is passionately in love with the Zagorskina girl. Listen.[3]

1

From early childhood, I recall, my soul
sought out the marvelous; I loved

---

[3] The poems thus clumsily interjected into the action ("I just chance to have a manuscript in my pocket") are youthful efforts which Lermontov never cared to include in his published *Poems*. They have here been englished quite literally and prosaically.

the world's illusions, but not the world itself,
where I lived for moments only—
moments of pure torment.
And I filled my secret dreams
with such moments; and yet the dreams,
like the world, could not be darkened by them.

2

How often, by the power of thought, I lived a whole
        lifetime
in one brief hour, and quite forgot
earth and the other life. And more than once,
made fearful by a melancholy dream,
I cried. And yet the creatures of my fancy—
the objects of imagined love or spite—
did not resemble earthly beings at all.
Of one piece they were made: all Heaven, or all Hell!

3

But for the beautiful, there is no grave!
When I am turned to dust, the astounded world
will bless my dreams, although it may not
understand them. And you, my angel—you,
along with me, will not know death. My love
will give you back eternal life;
and all men will repeat your name
with mine. Why should they separate the dead?

SNEGIN: He wrote that in a moment of inspiration! Read
me another.

ZARUTSKOY: This is addressed to the Zagorskina girl.

Oh why, with your enchanting smile,
do you arouse forgotten dreams?
I will be gay, but it is wrong for me:
the reason you know all too well.
We are not suited for each other.
You love the noisy and unfeeling world;
the Southland and the deserts claim my heart.
And you know happiness, which I cannot!
Your heavenly glance is beautiful,
like the early morning sky,
and shows how close you feel to everything.
But I'm a stranger to all things on earth!
My soul is frightened at the thought
of calling up the sacred past.
Its hopes are like the ravings of a stricken man;
and to believe in them, is to believe in dreams.
A solitary path has been laid out for me.
It has been cursed by a cruel fate;
and it is dark and dreary, like the thought
of happiness without you. Forgive me! Oh, forgive me,
      angel mine!

He felt everything he says in these poems. I like him
for that.

(*A clamor is heard from the next room.*)

A VOICE: Gentleman, I have the honor to announce that
we are assembled here for the burial rites of right thinking
and shame. Long live the fools and whores!

RYABINOV: A toast! Another toast! Copernicus was right:
the earth *does* revolve!

(*The noise lessens; then there is more applause.*[4] *Snegin and Zarutskoy go into the other room.*)

VISHNEVSKOY: Gentlemen! When will the Russians learn to be Russians?

CHELYAEV: When they go back a hundred years and make a clean start at enlightenment and education.

VYSHNEVSKOY: A fine solution! If your doctor wrote only such prescriptions as that, I'll wager you wouldn't be sitting at a table now. Instead, you'd be lying on a table.

ZARUTSKOY: In 1812, didn't we show that we are Russians? There hasn't been such an example since the world began. This generation doesn't really understand the significance of the great Moscow Fire. We cannot feel amazement at that feat. That idea, that feeling was born with the Russians. We should take pride in it, and leave amazement to posterity and the foreigners. Long live the Moscow Fire!

Scene V

[*January 10; morning. The study in Belinskoy's house; a fashionable decor. On the desk, an empty teacup and scattered ashes from a pipe.*]

BELINSKOY (*alone, walking back and forth in the room*): Fate will have it that I must marry. Well, what of that? Marriage is a very effective medicine for all kinds of dis-

---

[4] There is a brief abridgment of the text at this point; still another of those youthful poems (a free imitation of Byron's "The Dream," which Lermontov himself omitted from earlier drafts of the play) has been excised.

eases—especially for consumption of the pocketbook. I
have borrowed enough money to buy a country estate, if
I can get another thousand rubles. But where can I get it?
Marry! Marry! my reason shouts at me. All right. But
whom? Yesterday I met the Zagorskins. Natasha is very
sweet—very. She has something. But Vladimir is in love
with her. What does that matter? Possession is nine points
of the law. I am in such critical circumstances that he
should forgive me. Besides, I don't believe he really loves
her so very much. He is a strange, incomprehensible person: one day he is one thing, and the next day something
else. He contradicts himself. And yet he is always talking
you down and trying to convince you of something—naturally! It is an uncommon man who can stand up to him.
Then at other times you can't get a word out of him. He sits
there and says nothing. It's like a trance. His eyes remain
fixed, as though at that moment his whole existence had
come to a stop on one single idea. (*After a pause.*) However, I won't tell him anything about my intentions before
I have brought the business off. In the meantime, I'll go to
her house; and there, we'll see!

(*Arbenin enters, walking rapidly.*)

VLADIMIR: Belinskoy! Why so pensive?

BELINSKOY: Ah! Hello, Arbenin. I'm thinking about
plans . . . plans . . .

VLADIMIR: Hasn't fate cured you of making plans?

BELINSKOY: Oh, no! If I am firmly resolved to do something, I almost always succeed. Believe me: a man who
wants something at any cost, can compel fate to yield. Fate
is a woman.

VLADIMIR: As for me, I have so often been deceived by my desires, and so often had regrets after I achieved my aim, that now I don't desire anything at all. I just take life as it comes. I don't bother anybody. The result is that everybody tries to bother me in some way or other —to annoy me until I say something insulting to them. And do you know? Sometimes I enjoy it. I see people putting themselves under a great strain just to make my life still more unbearable in one way or another. Am I such an important person in the world? Or do their good offices extend even to the most insignificant people?

BELINSKOY: My friend, you are creating chimeras in your imagination, and then painting them black for greater romantic effect.

VLADIMIR: No, and again no! I tell you, I was not made to live with other people. I am too proud for them, and they are too petty for me.

BELINSKOY: So you weren't made to live with other people? On the contrary! You are very amiable when you're with other people. The ladies seek out your conversation; and the youngsters like you. It's true that sometimes you tell people—right to their faces—truths that are a bit too painful. But they forgive you anyway, because you talk to them intelligently, and somehow that becomes you.

VLADIMIR (*with a bitter smile*): I see. You want to console me.

BELINSKOY: When was the last time you were at the Zagorskins? Can they console you there?

VLADIMIR: I saw them yesterday. It's strange: she loves me, and she doesn't. Sometimes she is so good to me, so

sweet; and her eyes tell me so much . . . So much love
is expressed in that blush of modesty . . . And at other
times—especially at a ball, for instance—she is very different. Then I stop believing in her love, and in my own
happiness.

BELINSKOY: She is a coquette.

VLADIMIR: I don't believe it. There is a mystery in all
this . . .

BELINSKOY: The devil with your mysteries! It's very
simple. When your Natasha feels gay, she doesn't think of
you at all. But when she is bored, she finds you entertain-
ing. There is the whole of your mystery.

VLADIMIR: You said that with a tone of voice as tender as
though you were doing me a great benefit.

BELINSKOY (*shaking his head*): You're not yourself today.

VLADIMIR (*taking a torn letter out of his pocket*): Look
at this.

BELINSKOY: What is it?

VLADIMIR: It's a letter I wrote to her. Read it. Yesterday
I went to see her cousin, Princess Sophia. At a moment
when nobody was paying any attention to us, I asked her to
give this letter to Natasha. She agreed, but on condition
that she read it first. I gave it to her, and she went to
her room. The time I spent waiting for her to come back
was sheer torture. Suddenly she reappeared and told me
that my letter would amuse her cousin very much and
make her laugh. *Laugh?* Imagine that, my friend! I tore up
the letter, took my hat, and left.

BELINSKOY: I suspect the cunning of Princess Sophia.
Natasha would not laugh at a letter like that—because,

you see, I can easily guess its contents. It's a case of jealousy, and perhaps even something more. Or else just a joke.

VLADIMIR: It's deceit! Deceit! I saw *her*. I spent the entire evening with her, most of the time alone . . . I watched her at the theater. There were tears in her eyes during the performance of Schiller's *Intrigue and Love*. It is possible she could hear the story of my sufferings with indifference? (*He takes Belinskoy by the arm.*) What would happen if I could hold Natasha hard against my breast and tell her: "You are mine—mine forever!" Oh, God! I would never survive it! (*He looks closely at Belinskoy.*) Don't say a word! Don't destroy my childish hopes—not now! Later you can destroy them.

BELINSKOY: Later? (*Aside*) What's this? It is possible he has guessed his fate?

VLADIMIR: Oh, how our hearts can deceive us! (*Walks nervously back and forth.*)

BELINSKOY (*aside*): And must I destroy that illusion? Bah! I'm beginning to imitate him, apparently. No! That's nonsense! He doesn't love her as much as he seems to. Life is not a novel.

(*Belinskoy's Servant comes in.*)

SERVANT: Dmitry Vasilich, a peasant is here asking permission to see you. He says he heard that you were buying their village, and so he came—

BELINSKOY: Tell him to come in.

(*The Servant leaves. A moment later a gray-headed Peasant comes in and throws himself at Belinskoy's feet.*)

BELINSKOY: Stand up! Stand up! What can I do for you, my friend?

PEASANT (*on his knees*): We heard, master, that you wanted to buy us. And so I came . . . (*he bows his head*) We heard you were a good master.

BELINSKOY: Stand up, brother, and then speak. But stand up first!

PEASANT (*getting to his feet*): Don't be angry, *batyushka*, if I . . .

BELINSKOY: Go ahead and talk.

PEASANT (*bowing*): Master, the whole village sent me, an old man, to speak for them. I bow at your feet, hoping you will become our protector . . . All of us would pray to God for you. Be our savior!

BELINSKOY: What's this? You don't want to leave your mistress, do you?

PEASANT (*bowing at his feet*): Yes! Buy us! Buy us, *rodimoy!*

BELINSKOY (*aside*): A strange adventure! (*To the peasant*): Ah! So you are dissatisfied with your mistress?

PEASANT: Oh! Things are bad! It's because of our sins. (*Arbenin begins to listen.*)

BELINSKOY: Well, speak up, brother! What's the matter? Does the mistress deal harshly with you?

PEASANT: *Da tak, barin* . . . As God is good, we just can't stand it any more. We've put up with it for a long time, but now it's the end. We might just as well give up trying to live.

VLADIMIR: But what has she done? (*His face is dark with anger.*)

PEASANT: Why, whatever comes into her head.

BELINSKOY: Give us an example. Does she whip you often?

PEASANT: We get whipped, *batyushka,* and very hard, too . . . For every little thing, and sometimes for nothing at all. You see, the overseer stands in good with her. He does whatever he pleases. And if you don't take off your cap to him, God knows what he'll do to you! If you see him half a mile off, you have to take off your cap right away. And even in the middle of the day, when it's hot, you have to work with your cap off until he tells you to put it back on. And if he forgets to tell you, or if he has his temper up, you can work a whole day like that.

BELINSKOY: What abuse!

PEASANT: One time somebody told the mistress, "Fedka has said bad things about you and wants to make a complaint in town." Now Fedka was a fine man. But she ordered them to put him on the rack and pull his arms out of place. When they led him into the big yard, his wife and children cried. Then the men began to twist his arms. Fedka said to the overseer: "What did I ever do to you? You are killing me!" But the overseer just said, "Nonsense!" And they went on twisting his arms, and broke them. Fedka became a man without any arms. Now he just lies there on the stove and curses the day he was born.

BELINSKOY: But why doesn't somebody report her? A neighbor, for example. Or the town governor or police inspector? We have courts for things like that. It could go badly with your mistress.

PEASANT: Who will protect us poor people? The mistress has bribed all the judges—and she does it with the rent-money we pay her! Things are bad, *barin!* Things are very bad with us. Just look at the other village—it makes your heart bleed. Their life is quiet and happy. But we don't even sing any more at the evening meetings. The housemaids tell about one time when the mistress got her temper up at a servant girl. She took the scissors and stuck her, just like that! Oh, how it hurt! And sometimes she'll have a man's beard pulled out, hair by hair. *Batyushka!* It's enough to make you forget the holy saints! (*He falls on his knees before Belinskoy.*) Oh, if you helped us! Buy us! Buy us, *batyushka!* (*He weeps.*)

VLADIMIR (*enraged*): Humanity! Humanity! And woman—that creature sometimes so much like an angel—what crimes she is capable of! Oh, I curse your smiles, your happiness, your wealth—all bought with bloody tears! You stab people, break their arms, whip them, cut them, and pull out their beards hair by hair! Oh, God! At the very thought of it I feel pain in all my veins. I'd like to trample on every blood vessel of that monster—that woman! Just to hear this drives me to the point of madness!

BELINSKOY: It really is horrible.

PEASANT: Buy us, *rodimoy!*

VLADIMIR: Dmitry, do you have any money? Here is everything I have—a note for a thousand rubles. You can repay me some day. (*Puts the note on the desk.*)

BELINSKOY (*calculating*): In that case, I will try to buy the village . . . Run along, my good fellow, and tell your people they are out of danger. (*To Vladimir*) What a woman!

PEASANT: May God give happiness to both of you, masters. May He give you long life. May He give you everything your souls desire . . . *Proshchay, rodimoy!* (*He leaves.*)

VLADIMIR: O my country, my country! (*He paces rapidly back and forth.*)

BELINSKOY: How glad I am that I can buy that village now! How glad I am! This is the first time I have been able to help suffering humanity. It's a good cause. Those poor peasants! What a life, when every minute I am in danger of losing everything I have and falling into the hands of the hangmen!

VLADIMIR: There are people more deserving of sympathy than that peasant. Outer afflictions pass away. But the person who bears the whole cause of his suffering deep in his heart; in whom there lives a worm that devours the least little bits of pleasure; one who desires without hope, who is a burden to everybody—even those who love him— that person . . . but why talk about such people? No one can sympathize with them. And no one can understand them—no one at all.

BELINSKOY: Worrying about yourself again! Oh, you egotist! How can you compare chimeras with genuine miseries? Can the free man be compared to the slave?

VLADIMIR: One is the slave of mankind, the other the slave of fate. The former can wait for a kind master, or he may have a choice. But the latter, never! He is the plaything of blind chance. His own passions and the unfeelingness of others—all conspire for his ruin.

BELINSKOY: Then you don't believe in Providence? Do you deny the existence of a God who knows all and governs all?

VLADIMIR (*looking upward*): Do I believe? Do I believe?

BELINSKOY: I can see that your head is stuffed full of false ideas.

VLADIMIR (*after a pause*): Listen! The weather is fine now, isn't it? Let's go out on the boulevard.

BELINSKOY: You're an odd one!

(*Mar'ya Dmitrevna's Servant enters.*)

What do you want? Who are you?

VLADIMIR: My mother's servant!

SERVANT: Mar'ya Dmitrevna sent me to you, *suda'r*. I spent half an hour looking for you at three different houses where you often visit, so they told me.

VLADIMIR: What has happened?

SERVANT: My mistress—

VLADIMIR: What about her?

SERVANT: She has taken very sick and wants you to come to her at once.

VLADIMIR: Sick, you say? Sick?

SERVANT: Very sick.

VLADIMIR (*thoughtfully*): Very! Yes, I will go! (*Holding out his hand to Belinskoy.*) I am firm in my afflictions, isn't that true? (*During the foregoing remarks his face has changed, and his voice falters. He leaves.*)

BELINSKOY (*watching him go*): Your hypersensitivity will be the ruin of you! You want peace, but you don't know how to enjoy it. If it ever came to you, it would be your greatest torment.

I am usually of a cheerful disposition, but I have noticed that Arbenin's melancholy is contagious. After seeing him, it takes me an hour or two to recover. Ha, ha, ha! I'll test the faithfulness of that woman! We'll see whether Natasha can resist my attacks. If she betrays Arbenin, it will be the best way to cure him of a very stupid disease.

(*Belinskoy's servant comes in.*)

What do you want?

SERVANT: I went to the theater for the ticket, as you told me to. Here it is, sir.

BELINSKOY: Good! In the first row? Fine! (*To himself*) It will be boring tonight at the French Theater. Their acting is stiff, stuffy, and generally vile. But what can I do? All the *beau monde* will be there. (*He lights his pipe and leaves.*)

Scene VI

[*January 10; afternoon. At the Zagorskins; the young ladies' room. Princess Sophia is sitting on the bed. Natasha is in front of a mirror, fixing her hair.*]

SOPHIA: *Ma chère cousine,* I must warn you to be careful.

NATASHA: No instructions, please! I know what I'm doing. I will never show Arbenin any great marks of favor. He'll have to be content with little ones.

SOPHIA: You'll never force him to marry you. He's not that kind of man.

NATASHA: Naturally, I won't pursue him. But if he loves me, I'll marry him.

SOPHIA (*mockingly*): He is very interesting, isn't he? And what nice eyes he has—all full of tears!

NATASHA: Yes, for me he's very interesting.

SOPHIA: Take my word for it, he's only playing games with you, because he's convinced you are in love with him.

NATASHA: There's no reason why he should be convinced.

SOPHIA: Just try acting cool toward him, and he'll leave off immediately.

NATASHA: I have tried it already, and he didn't leave off. He has only loved me the more ever since.

SOPHIA: But you don't know how to dissemble. You—

NATASHA: I'm just as good at it as you are, believe me.

SOPHIA: Last year, Arbenin was courting Polina Lidina in the same way he's courting you now. Then he suddenly dropped her, and he himself laughed at her. Remember? And the same thing will happen to you.

NATASHA: I'm not Polina.

SOPHIA: We'll see.

NATASHA: But why do you keep on this subject all the time?

SOPHIA: Because I know what I know. Yesterday—

NATASHA: What happened? No, don't tell me.

SOPHIA: Arbenin was at our house yesterday.

NATASHA: And?

SOPHIA: He was flirting with Liza Shumova—telling her all kinds of stories. And at the same time he asked me to give you a letter from him. That's just like a man! Infatuated with one girl, and writing letters to another! After that, can you go on believing what he says? I read the letter and gave it back to him. I said you would find it very amusing. He tore it up and left. What a farce! (*Pause*) And besides, I've been assured that he goes around boasting you have shown him special signs of affection. But I don't believe it.

NATASHA (*aside*): He's behaving stupidly! Oh, I'm so angry with him for that! Boasting! Who would have thought it? This is too much! (*Aloud*) You know, cousin, Belinskoy was here last evening. *Un jeune homme charmant!* So handsome, so intelligent, and so charming—really delightful. He's not one to go about sulking. And so well-bred—just as though he'd spent his whole life at court.

SOPHIA: Congratulations! And I trust he was very taken with you? (*Aside*) I'm elated! My words are having an effect. (*Aloud*) Yesterday, at our house, Arbenin almost had a quarrel with Nelidov. You know how Nelidov is —quiet, staid, and cautious. And Vladimir doesn't particularly care for that type. They were talking about society and the importance of reputation. Nelidov repeated several times that he valued his good name. From the way he said it, it was easy to see he was hinting that Arbenin had lost his own good name. Vladimir got his meaning, and his face went all pale. Later, he said to me, "Nelidov was trying to wound my vanity, and he succeeded. It's true that I am lost to society . . . But I am just proud enough to appear quite indifferent when I hear the fact mentioned." Ha, ha, ha! That shows real strength of character, doesn't it, Natasha?

NATASHA: Of course! Vladimir doesn't entirely deserve

the bad opinion people have of him. But he really doesn't care much. And Nelidov behaved very stupidly when he tried to insult him. (*Natasha goes to the window.*)

SOPHIA: Vladimir is just as much offended by malicious talk as the next person, believe me. Only he doesn't want to show it.

(*There is a pause of some duration.*)

NATASHA (*with some excitement*): Ah! Here comes Belinskoy!

Scene VII

[*February 3; morning. The study of Pavel Grigorich Arbenin. He is seated in an armchair. A middle-aged man with gray whiskers, wearing an overcoat, is standing across from him.*]

PAVEL GRIGORICH: No, and again no! Tell your master that I have no intention of waiting. If a man owes a debt, he must pay. If he lacks the means to do it, he shouldn't have acquired the debt in the first place. In Russia, we have courts for such things. And what if I were poor? Does it mean nothing that I have waited two months?

THE AGENT: Just two weeks, *suda'r:* We'll be getting some money from the plant any day, now. Do you think we are deceiving you?

PAVEL GRIGORICH: Not for one single day will I wait!

THE AGENT: But where can we get the money? Eight thousand rubles can't just be picked up in the street.

PAVEL GRIGORICH: Then let your master sell you, if he has to. But he's going to pay me on time. And with interest, do you understand?

THE AGENT: Have mercy!

PAVEL GRIGORICH: Not a word more! Get along with you! *(The agent leaves.)* What a sly one! As though everybody should wait for him! Oh, no, my good fellow! Money is scarce now, and grain is cheap. Not only that, but the crops aren't doing well. Let the counts' sons and the big aristocrats squander their estates if they want to! We ordinary gentry will only gain the more for it. Let them spend their time at court, or bowing and scraping in the salons with their chamberlain's keys.[5] We'll go more slowly, but we'll rise higher. And one fine day, when it's already too late, they'll look around and see that we have caught up with them. *(He gets up from the armchair.)* Oof! These business affairs have worn me out! Still, there's something about it that makes you feel good. You look at a piece of paper in front of you—a piece of paper that contains in itself the price of many people—and you think: Through my own efforts I have achieved a method of exchanging people for paper. And why not? A man decomposes, just as paper does. And, like paper, he bears identifying marks that set him above others. Without them . . . *(he yawns.)* Oof! I'm sleepy. But where is my son? He's probably acquired some new debts, because he's been taking dinner at home for

5 The court chamberlains, or *Kammerherrs*, had access to the Tsar's chambers—a right that was symbolized by a gold key. The key was often worn on a blue ribbon: or it might be embroidered on the back of the chamberlain's dress uniform.

three days now. That's the way it goes. I'd much rather not have any children, thank you very much.

(Vladimir comes quickly into the room. He is pale.)

VLADIMIR *(speaking in a loud voice)*: Batyushka!

PAVEL GRIGORICH: What is it?

VLADIMIR: I have come to . . . I have a request to make of you. Just one. Don't refuse me . . . Come with me! Come! One minute's delay, and you will regret it, I swear you will!

PAVEL GRIGORICH: But where do you want me to go with you? You've lost your wits.

VLADIMIR: And for good reason. If you had seen what I've seen, and then didn't lose your own wits, I'd be very much surprised.

PAVEL GRIGORICH: This kind of behavior is unheard of! Vladimir, you are trying my patience!

VLADIMIR: So you don't want to go with me? So you don't believe me? And I thought . . . But now I must tell all. Listen to me. A certain woman, who is dying, wants to see you. That woman—

PAVEL GRIGORICH: What do I have to do with her?

VLADIMIR: She is your wife.

PAVEL GRIGORICH *(angrily)*: Vladimir!

VLADIMIR: You seem to think that with your stern look you can frighten me and silence the voice of nature in my breast. But I'm not like you. That same voice which commands me to obey you, compels me to hate you! Yes, to hate you, if you continue to reject my mother's appeals! Oh! The things that have happened today have wiped out all of my fears. I can speak straight out. I am your son and hers. You are happy. She is agonizing on her deathbed. Who is right and who is wrong, is not my concern. I have heard her prayers and sobbing. The lowest beggar in the world would call me a scoundrel if I could still love you!

PAVEL GRIGORICH: How dare you? I have long since ceased to expect love from you. But when did a son ever reproach a father with such words? Get out of my sight!

VLADIMIR: I have already begged you not to destroy in me the last spark of a son's obedience, so that I don't repeat these accusations before the whole world.

PAVEL GRIGORICH: Great God! What have I lived to witness? (*To Vladimir*) Do you know—

VLADIMIR: I know. You yourself are racked by your conscience. You do not have a moment of peace. You are guilty of a great deal—

PAVEL GRIGORICH: Hold your tongue!

VLADIMIR: I won't. I didn't come here to beg, but to demand. Yes, to demand! I have that right. I must. Her tears have cut deep into my memory. Father! (*He goes down on his knees.*) *Batyushka!* Come with me!

PAVEL GRIGORICH: Get up! (*He is alarmed.*)

VLADIMIR: Then you will come?

PAVEL GRIGORICH (*aside*): What if it's really true? Perhaps—

VLADIMIR: Then you refuse? (*He stands.*)

PAVEL GRIGORICH (*aside*): She is dying, Vladimir says. She wants to obtain my pardon . . . That's true. And I would . . . But to go there? If it became known, what would people say?

VLADIMIR: You have nothing to fear. My mother is dying right now. She wants to make peace with you, but not in order to live under your name. She wants to be sure, before she goes to her grave, that she does not have a single enemy on this earth. That's all she is asking for—all she prays for. You have refused. But there is a Judge in Heaven.

Your feat was a fine one: it showed firmness of character. People will praise you for it. And what does it matter if among a thousand praises, one voice of accusation can be heard? (*He smiles bitterly.*)

PAVEL GRIGORICH (*stiffly*): Leave me!

VLADIMIR: Very well, I'll go. I'll go and say that you can't come—that you're busy. (*Bitterly.*) For one last time in her life, she will have believed in a hope! (*He goes quietly to the door.*) Oh, if only a thunderbolt would strike me down on this threshold! What? Shall I go to her alone? I will become the murderer of my own mother. (*He pauses and looks at his father.*) Great God! There is a man for you!

PAVEL GRIGORICH (*to himself*): And yet, why shouldn't I go? What harm can it do? To be reconciled before death is nothing—nobody would laugh at that. And everything would be better. Yes, so be it! I'll go. Probably she is unconscious and won't recognize me . . . I'll tell her I forgive her, and that will be the end of it. (*Aloud*) Vladimir! Listen to me! wait! (*Vladimir approaches him, mistrustfully*). I'll go with you! I have made up my mind. Nobody will see us, will they? I believe you. Only take care, another time, and think what you're saying.

VLADIMIR: So you really want to go and see my mother? You really do? That's hard for me to believe. Tell me: You really do?

PAVEL GRIGORICH: Really.

VLADIMIR (*throwing his arms around him*): I have a father! I have a father again! (*He starts to cry.*) Oh, God! I'm happy again. How light my heart is now! I have a father! I can see, now . . . I can see that it is hard to oppose our natural feelings. Oh, how happy I am! Don't you see, *batyushka,* what a fine thing it is to do . . . to decide to do good? Your eyes have brightened. Your face has become the face of an angel. (*He embraces him again.*) Oh, Father, God will reward you! Let's go—let's go right away. We must get there while she is still alive.

PAVEL GRIGORICH (*aside, as he is about to go*): And so, I must see her . . . Very well! But isn't there some trap here? Still, Vladimir is so desperate . . . But isn't it easy for a woman—and especially my wife—to deceive anybody at all? Oh, I felt something was wrong! I have seen through this plot, and now everything is clear. She wants to decoy me again, and then start coaxing . . . And if I don't agree, my son will tell the whole city how cruel I was. She will probably incite him to it. A very cunning scheme, I must admit. Most cunning! But they tried it on the wrong person. It's a good thing I figured it out in time! I won't go—not me! Let her die, if she was able to live without me!

VLADIMIR: You are delaying!

PAVEL GRIGORICH (*coldly*): Yes, I am delaying.

VLADIMIR: You . . . That change! You—

PAVEL GRIGORICH (*stiffly*): I am staying here! You can tell your mother—my former wife—that I did not fall into the trap that had been set for me, as I did once before. Tell her that I thank her for the invitation and wish her a happy journey. (*Vladimir shudders and steps back.*)

VLADIMIR: What? (*In desperation.*) This goes beyond all my expectations! And with such out-and-out coldness! With such an evil smile! And I am your son? Yes, I am your son. And therefore I must be the enemy of all that is sacred—your enemy—out of gratitude! Oh, if I could put all my feelings, my heart, my soul, my breath, into one single word—into one sound—that sound would be a curse on the first moment of my life! It would be a thunderbolt that would shake your very entrails, Father, and cure you forever of calling me "son"!

PAVEL GRIGORICH: Quiet, you madman! Have a care for my wrath! Just you wait. Calmer days will come, when you will learn how dangerous it is to insult a father. And I will give you punishment to make an example of you!

VLADIMIR (*covering his face with his hands*): And I was hoping for mercy!

PAVEL GRIGORICH: Ungrateful wretch! Monster! Aren't you indebted to me? To accuse me like that!

VLADIMIR: Ungrateful? You gave me life. Take it back! Take it back, if you can! Oh, what a bitter gift!

PAVEL GRIGORICH: Out of my house this instant! And don't you dare come back until my poor spouse has died! (*He laughs.*) Let's just see how soon you come back. Let's see whether she has a real illness that will take her to the grave—or whether it was just clumsy scheming that caused so much uproar and made you forget your obligations and respect. And now, go! Think hard about the way you have behaved, and remember the things you have said. Then, if you dare, show yourself to my eyes again! (*He looks wrathfully at his son, goes out, and closes the door behind him.*)

VLADIMIR (*during a brief interval of silence he has been standing stock still, looking at the door through which his father left*): Everything is finished!

(*He goes out through the other door, complete hopelessness evident in all of his movements. He leaves the door open; and for some time he can be seen pacing rapidly, then stopping. Finally, with a helpless gesture, he leaves.*)

Scene VIII

[*February 3, late morning. Mar'ya Dmitrevna's bedroom. A table with bottles of medicine. Mar'ya Dmitrevna is in bed. Annushka is standing near her.*]

ANNUSHKA: You have a high fever, *sudarynya.* Wouldn't you like some hot tea or some elderberry potion? Ah, my dear, your hands are so cold! They're like ice. Shouldn't I send for the doctor?

MAR'YA DMITREVNA: What is pressing on my breast?

ANNUSHKA: Nothing, *sudarynya.* The blanket is very light. Why should it weigh on you?

MAR'YA DMITREVNA: Annushka! Today I am going to die!

ANNUSHKA: Come now, Mar'ya Dmitrevna! You'll get better. God is good. Why should you die?

MAR'YA DMITREVNA: Why?

ANNUSHKA: Sick people don't always die. Sometimes the healthy ones go to the other world before the sick ones. Isn't it time to take your medicine?

MAR'YA DMITREVNA: I don't want any medicine . . . Where is my son? But I forgot—I sent him away myself. Look out the window, to see whether he's coming now. Go to the window . . . What? He isn't coming? How long it has been!

ANNUSHKA: The street is empty.

MAR'YA DMITREVNA (*to herself*): He will persuade his father—I'm sure he will! Oh, how sweet to be reconciled before the end! Now I'm not ashamed to look him in the face! (*Somewhat louder.*) Annushka! Why are you looking out of the window like that?

ANNUSHKA: Nothing. I just—

MAR'YA DMITREVNA: Come, tell me the truth. What is it?

ANNUSHKA: A funeral procession, *sudarynya.* And such a fancy one! So many carriages following behind! And the hearse-cloth is so splendid! Two bishops! And choristers! I just can't describe it.

MAR'YA DMITREVNA: Annushka, my time has come, too. I feel the last moment is near. Oh, Heavenly Father, let it be soon!

ANNUSHKA: Enough, *sudarynya!* Why so eager? If you should die—which God forbid! what would happen to me? Who would have a thought for me? Would Pavel Grigorich take me into his household? That would never happen. Anyway, it would be better to go out begging. Kind folk will always give a body something to eat.

MAR'YA DMITREVNA: My son Vladimir will not abandon you.

ANNUSHKA: But how will he ever bear it, if you should die? You yourself know what a hot-headed one he is! A mere nothing can throw him into a rage . . . And then God help us!

MAR'YA DMITREVNA: You're right. I must reward you. In my money-box you will find eighty rubles. Give a few to the old man, Pavel. He has always served me faithfully. And I have always been very content with you—always. (*An expression of troubled happiness shows on Annushka's face.*) Oh, how my heart is pounding! Which is worse—anticipation, or hopelessness?

(*The door opens, and Vladimir comes in quietly, his expression one of dark despair. He goes to the foot of the bed and stands there, saying nothing.*)

ANNUSHKA: Vladimir Pavlovich has come!

MAR'YA DMITREVNA (*rapidly*): He has come! (*She raises her head, and then lets it fall back.*) Vladimir . . . You are alone! And I thought . . . You are alone!

VLADIMIR: Yes.

MAR'YA DMITREVNA: My son! You asked him to come here? You said I was dying? Will he come soon?

VLADIMIR (*darkly*): How are you feeling? Are you strong enough to talk . . . and to listen?

ANNUSHKA: Vladimir Pavlovich, the mistress cried all the time you were gone.

VLADIMIR: Oh, God, God! You are almighty! Why must I be the one to kill my mother?

MAR'YA DMITREVNA: Hurry up and tell me. Don't tear me apart bit by bit. Is your father coming? (*He does not answer.*) Where is he? . . . How can I face God? . . . Vladimir! Without him I can never die in peace!

VLADIMIR (*quietly*): No.

MAR'YA DMITREVNA (*She has not heard him*): What did you say? Give me your hand, Vladimir.

VLADIMIR (*He begins to cry. He drops to his knees besides the bed and covers her hand with kisses*): I am near you. Why do you need anyone else? Aren't you content with me? Does anyone love you more than I do?

MAR'YA DMITREVNA: Get up . . . Are you crying?

VLADIMIR (*He rises, and walks off a way*): A horrible torture! If I can endure all this, I will consider myself an unfeeling stone not worthy of the name of a man! If I can endure it, I'll be convinced that the son always takes after the father—that his blood flows in my veins, and that I desired her death, just as he did. So! I will have to drag him here by force, and frighten and threaten him into forgiving her! (*With mad gaiety.*) Listen! Listen to what I have to tell you! My father is in good spirits, quite healthy, and unwilling to see you! (*He suddenly stops, as if frightened.*)

MAR'YA DMITREVNA (*She shudders, and there is a pause*): Pray . . . Pray for us . . . He didn't want to . . . Oh!

ANNUSHKA: It's going badly with her.

MAR'YA DMITREVNA: No, no! I'll gather my last strength . . . Vladimir, you must hear everything and judge your parents. Come closer. I am dying. I shall give up my soul to a just God. I don't want you, my only son, to accuse me from hearsay. I will pronounce my own sentence. (*A pause.*) I am guilty. My fault was to be young. I had a passionate nature, and your father treated me coldly. Before, I had loved another. If my husband had wanted it that way, I would have forgotten the past. For some years I tried to conquer my feelings; but one moment decided my fate . . . Don't look at me like that! I'd rather you reproached me with the harshest words! I am the evildoer who has hurt you. My offense makes me loathe myself . . . and not myself alone. I paid for that offense with long years of repentance. Listen to me. It was a secret. But I did not want to—I could not—quiet my conscience. I myself told your father everything. With bitter tears, with humility, I threw myself at his feet. I hoped he would be generous and forgive me . . . But he drove me out of the house. I had to leave you, a mere child. And in silence, weighed down by the heaviness of my own guilt, I had to endure the derision of the world . . . He dealt harshly with me . . . I am dying . . . If he does not forgive me, God will punish him . . . Vladimir? Do you condemn your mother? You aren't looking at me! (*Toward the end, her voice has become increasingly weaker.*)

VLADIMIR (*very wrought up; to himself*): I see! I see! Nature is armed against me! I bear within myself the seeds of evil. I was created to destroy the natural order! Great God in Heaven! My mother lies here dying, and I don't have one word of consolation for her—not one! Can my heart really be so cold that I cannot shed a single tear for her? May evil fall upon the one who made my heart that cold! He is taking out his vengeance on me.

Through him, I have become a criminal. From this moment on, may I never more feel pity! Day and night, I will sing to my father a hideous song—until his hair stands on end and repentance begins to gnaw at his soul! (*Turns to his mother.*) Oh, my angel! Don't die so quickly! Just a few hours more!

ANNUSHKA (*looking at her mistress with obvious alarm*): Vladimir Pavlovich! (*He hears her, and looks at her closely. She reaches out a hand to Mar'ya Dmitrevna, and then suddenly stops.*) May God have mercy on her soul! (*She crosses herself.*) (*Vladimir shudders, sways on his feet, and almost falls. He supports himself against the back of a chair, remaining immobile in this position for some time.*) How quietly the dear thing passed away! What will become of me now?

VLADIMIR (*approaches the body and, after one look, quickly turns away*): For such a soul, and such a death, tears mean nothing! I have no tears. But I will avenge her! I will avenge her! I will avenge her pitilessly and horribly! I will go to my father with the news of her death. I will compel him, force him, to weep. And when he starts to weep . . . I will laugh! (*He runs out. There is a long pause.*)

ANNUSHKA: So her own son has left her! Now everything I can lay hands on is mine! And where's the harm? Better I should have it than somebody else. And Vladimir Pavlovich doesn't need it. (*She holds a mirror to the lips of the dead woman.*) The mirror is unclouded. She has breathed her last. How pale she is!

(*She leaves the room and calls for the other servants to come and make preparations for the rites.*)

Scene IX

[*February 3, afternoon. A room at the Zagorskins'. Natasha and Princess Sophia. Anna Nikolavna enters with Two Old Ladies.*]

ANNA NIKOLAVNA: I wasn't expecting you at all today! Please come in and sit down. How is your health, Marfa Ivanovna? (*They sit down.*)

FIRST OLD LADY: *Ekh, mat' moya!* What kind of health do I have? Always rheumatism and a swollen face. I only just now took the compress off my cheek. (*To the other Old Lady.*) What a coincidence, Katerina Dmitrevna! Just as I arrived in front of the house, along you came, as though we had planned to visit Anna Nikolavna together!

SECOND OLD LADY (*to the hostess*): I heard you had been ill.

ANNA NIKOLAVNA: Yes, I have been. Thank you for coming. I'm better now. Well, have you heard anything new?

SECOND OLD LADY: My Yegorushka, you know, is in Petersburg. He writes me that our troops have given the Turks a sound thrashing. And they captured a pasha!

FIRST OLD LADY: Thanks be to God! By the way, I heard that Gorinkin has married. And just guess who the bride was! Did you know Bolotina? It's her daughter. A fine catch! She had so many suitors. But there you are. Some people are just lucky!

ANNA NIKOLAVNA: And I heard that Count Svitskoy died. He left a wife and children, you know.

FIRST OLD LADY: Oh? What a pity! . . . And the things they are saying! Have you heard?

ANNA NIKOLAVNA: What?

SECOND OLD LADY: Yes, what is it? It's odd I haven't heard yet.

FIRST OLD LADY: They say that the Count—may God forgive him—sold almost his entire estate and gave the money to his natural children. Such people there are in this world! And they're saying, too, that in his will he directed them not to spend more than a hundred rubles on his funeral.

SECOND OLD LADY: Well, what can you expect? What is bred in the bone will never come out in the flesh. He was always an odd one, God rest his soul! And did they follow the instructions in his will?

FIRST OLD LADY: Indeed not! He might just as well have directed them to toss him into a gully. No, *matushka:* his funeral cost five thousand rubles. Services were held at the Donsky Monastery, and there were two bishops.

ANNA NIKOLAVNA: It must have been very elegant, then.

NATASHA: As though it made any difference!

FIRST OLD LADY: What? Do you think a count can have the same kind of funeral as a beggar?

SECOND OLD LADY (*after a general silence*): Anna Niko-lavna, you must excuse me. I only came to see you for a minute. I must run off to my sister-in-law's for a christen-ing. (*She rises.*) *Proschayte!*

ANNA NIKOLAVNA: If that's the way it is, I won't try to

keep you. (*They kiss.*) *Do svidan'ya, matushka.* (*She takes her to the door.*)

FIRST OLD LADY: Well, what do you think of that? How dressed up our Mavra Petrovna was! Crimson ribbons on her hat! Do you think that's proper? Why, she can hardly drag herself around! How old would you say she was, Anna Nikolavna?

ANNA NIKOLAVNA: She's fifty—or so she says.

FIRST OLD LADY: She's cheating by ten years. Why, her children were already growing up when I was married!

NATASHA (*quietly, to Sophia*): I suspect that's because she was married at thirty.

SOPHIA: Why do you bother listening to them, Natasha?

NATASHA: Why? Because it's very amusing.

(*A Servant comes in.*)

SERVANT: Dmitry Vasilich Belinskoy has come.

ANNA NIKOLAVNA: What does this mean? (*To the Servant.*) Show him in to the drawing room. (*The Servant leaves.*)

(*Quietly, to the* OLD LADY): Come along with me, *matushka.* I can guess why he has come! In fact, I've already been told. He himself is not so very wealthy. But his uncle doesn't have long to live, and he owns fifteen hundred souls.

FIRST OLD LADY: I understand what you mean. (*Aside.*) Let's see what this Belinskoy is like. (*To Natasha.*) Oh, you sly one!

(*They both leave.*)

SOPHIA: Why are you blushing so?

NATASHA: I?

SOPHIA (*with a wave of the hand*): Come, now! One would think you were mesmerized. Natasha! Your cheeks are burning. You're all atremble. You've quite lost your self-possession. What does this mean?

NATASHA (*taking her hand*): It's nothing. Who said I was trembling? Ah, do you know something? I have guessed why he has come! Now everything will be decided, isn't that right?

SOPHIA: What will be decided?

NATASHA: What stupid questions, cousin! Yesterday the Princess was here, and—

SOPHIA: Now I see. You are in love with Belinskoy. Well, what of that? (NATASHA *turns away*.) It's very natural.

NATASHA (*excitedly*): Listen to me! He is so kind—so charming!

SOPHIA: Poor Arbenin!

NATASHA: Why do you say that?

SOPHIA: He loves you so! Belinskoy has come to ask for your hand. And you probably won't refuse him, isn't that so? But I know that Arbenin loves you very, very much. (*She smiles mockingly.*)

NATASHA: He'll just have to get over it. Besides, he was quite capable of playing games with others; perhaps he was playing games with me, too. Who can guarantee that he wasn't? It's quite true that at first I rather liked him. There's something unusual about him . . . But on the other hand, what an insufferable character he has! And what a malicious turn of thought! And such gloomy imaginings! Good Heavens! A man like that would make life miserable for you before one week was up. There are many others who feel just as deeply as he does, but still they are cheerful.

SOPHIA: You'd like to go on laughing at things. (*She looks at her closely*.) Late yesterday afternoon, Arbenin came to our house. He sat at the piano and improvised for half an hour. I was listening. Suddenly he jumped up and came over to me. There were tears in his eyes. "What's the matter?" I asked. "A fit!" he answered, smiling bitterly. "The music made me think of Italy. In all the frozen expanse of Russia there isn't a single heart that might respond to mine. Everyone I love flees from me. Do I ask for pity? No! I am like someone stricken with the plague. Everyone who loves me is infected with that disease of unhappiness that I am obliged to call life!" Then he watched me closely, as though expecting an answer. And I guessed . . . But you aren't listening to me!

NATASHA: Please leave me. What do I need with your Arbenin? Do whatever you want with him. I swear to you, I won't be jealous. Listen! Someone is coming. It must be mama.

SOPHIA (*aside*): Heaven is fulfilling my wish to perfection! Fate is avenging me! Good! He will feel all the weight of my hopeless, disappointed love. I had good cause for encouraging Natasha to grow cool towards him. This delights me. And yet, what is the good of it for me? I have taken my vengeance—but for what? He doesn't know how much I love him. But he will know! I will show him what a woman is!

(ANNA NIKOLAVNA *enters.*)

ANNA NIKOLAVNA: Natasha, come! I want to speak to you about something important—something that will decide the course of your life. Getting married is no trifling matter. Your entire future depends upon one moment. Your heart must cast the die; but reason, too, must have its say. Now think carefully. Belinskoy has asked for your hand. Do you agree, or not? Do you like him?

NATASHA (*confused*): I . . . I don't know.

ANNA NIKOLAVNA: What do you mean, you don't know? He is waiting in the other room. Who should know if you don't? Make up your mind quickly—and at least give him hopes. Why don't you say something? He is an honorable, well-bred young man. He has an estate—and you know that ours has been dissipated. Besides, he will come into a rich inheritance. Just think: fifteen hundred souls! Use your head. You are already grown up. You'll soon be nineteen. If you don't get married now, perhaps you never will. Do you want to be an old maid? Things are bad now—there are no marriageable men in Moscow. The young ones with money don't want to get married. They just want to enjoy themselves. And the old ones— what do they have to offer? They're either stupid or poor. Make up your mind, Natasha. He's waiting. Come, now, and tell me the truth: Do you like him?

NATASHA: Yes.

ANNA NIKOLAVNA: So you agree, then. I'll go—

NATASHA (*stopping her mother*): *Maman*, wait! It's all happening so quickly! I swear it all seems like a dream . . . How can I make up my mind in one minute? (*There*

are tears in her eyes; she covers her face with her hands.)
I can't! Does it have to be right this minute?

ANNA NIKOLAVNA (*in caressing tones*): Calm yourself,
my dear. What are you crying for? Didn't you yourself say
that you liked him? Just see how your heart is pounding!
That's not good for your health. You are all wrought up.
I acted rashly. Still, you'll have to make up your mind.
Remember, he's waiting. It isn't good to let a suitor
get away. Of course I'm not forcing you—I'm just asking.
Do you agree? Then I'll tell him right away. If not, then
not. It's no great harm.

NATASHA (*drying her tears*): I like him! It's just that
. . . Give him hope. Tell him he can come here as a
suitor. But no more than that. I just don't know . . .
You told me so quickly . . . I don't know . . . I'm
ashamed of crying over nothing. *Maman!* You know how
to tell him . . . I'll agree to anything.

ANNA NIKOLAVNA: Well, it's about time! What are you
crying about, my angel? (*Crosses her.*) Christ be with you!
Good luck!

(*She leaves.*)

NATASHA: Oh!

SOPHIA: You are so pale, cousin! But let me congratulate you. You're engaged!

NATASHA: How quickly it all happened!

(*She goes out.*)

SOPHIA: Quite true. When we want something, and
our desire is fulfilled, it always seems to us that it has
been fulfilled too quickly. We would rather contemplate
joy in the future than in the past. She is happy . . . And

I? But why have regrets? People are innocent if fate un-expectedly gratifies their selfish desires. Therefore, they are justified. Therefore, my heart should be at peace. It should have been at peace!

Scene X

[*February 4, evening. A room in Pavel Grigorich's house; Servants are lighting the lamps.*]

FIRST SERVANT: It seems he wasn't in his right mind. He hadn't recovered yet from what happened yesterday.

SECOND SERVANT: What did the master say to him?

THIRD SERVANT: "My curse upon you!" is what he said.

SECOND: Vladimir Pavlovich didn't deserve that.

FIRST: And where is the old master?

THIRD: He went out for the evening.

SECOND: Was he upset when you were helping him dress?

THIRD: Not a bit of it. He didn't strike me even once. Cursing his son and going out for the evening—for him, these two things are as much alike as drinking a glass of wine and a glass of water.

FIRST: The young master had hard words for his father. At first the shock was too much for the old man.

SECOND: It's always like that. But it's a sorry business. *Ey bogu!* It's a sorry business. A father's curse is no jok-ing matter. Better a person should have a millstone on his heart.

THIRD: Ivan has been ordered not to let the boy out of

his sight. There's a father for you! First he curses his son; and now he's afraid the boy will lay hands on himself.

SECOND: Blood will tell.

THIRD: To my way of thinking, it's better to kill a man than curse him.

Scene XI

[*February 4, evening. Vladimir's room. The moon is shining in the window. Vladimir is standing near the desk, one hand resting on it. Ivan is near the door.*]

IVAN: Are you feeling well, *sudar'?*

VLADIMIR: Why?

IVAN: You are pale.

VLADIMIR: I'm pale? I'll be even paler some of these days.

IVAN: Your father lost his temper, that's all. He'll soon forgive you.

VLADIMIR: Run along, like a good fellow. That doesn't concern you.

IVAN: I've been ordered not to leave you.

VLADIMIR: You're lying! There's no one here who would care that much what happened to me. Leave me! I am quite well.

IVAN: It's no use, *sudar'*, to try to convince me of that. Your nervous look, the way your eyes keep staring off somewhere, and the way your voice shakes—all that proves just the opposite.

VLADIMIR (*He takes out his purse; to himself*): They tell me that with money you can do anything with human beings. (*Aloud.*) Take this, and run along. There are thirty gold pieces in it.

IVAN: Judas sold Our Saviour for thirty pieces of silver, and those coins you have there are gold. No, *barin,* I'm not such a man. I may be a slave, but I will not take money for such a service.

VLADIMIR (*He throws the purse at the window, breaking the pane. The glass tinkles, and the purse falls into the street*): Then let somebody pick it up!

IVAN: What is happening to you, *barin?* Don't take things so hard. Not all grief—

VLADIMIR: I must insist . . .

IVAN: May God send you happiness, if only because you have been good to me. Never, so help me God, have I heard an angry word from you.

VLADIMIR: Is that true?

IVAN: I always tell my wife and children to pray for you.

VLADIMIR (*absently*): So you have a wife and children?

IVAN: And a fine family they are! Straight from Heaven . . . A good wife . . . And the little ones! It warms your heart just to look at them!

VLADIMIR: If I have treated you well, do me one favor.

IVAN: I am ready in body and soul, *batyushka,* to do your bidding.

VLADIMIR (*taking him by the arm*): You have children . . . Never, never curse them! (*He walks over to the window; Ivan watches him with pity.*) But he, my father, cursed me—and at a moment when I could have died from the effect of his words! But I did my duty. *She* will justify me before the Almighty. Now I shall test the last thing remaining for me on earth: the love of a woman. Oh God, how little you have left to me! The last thread tying me to life will break, and I will be with you. You created my heart for Yourself: the curse of a man has no effect on Your wrath. You are merciful, or else I shouldn't have been born. (*He looks out the window.*) That moon up there, and those stars—how hard they are trying to convince me that life means nothing! Where are all of my tremendous schemes? What was the use of my thirsting after great things? All is gone—I see that now. In the same way, a cloud in the evening sky, before the sun touches the horizon, takes on the aspect of a celestial city, its golden edges all aglitter, and promises miracles to the imagination. But the sun goes down, the wind blows, the cloud lengthens out, darkens, and finally falls to the earth in the form of dew!

Scene XII

[*February —, evening. A room at the Zagorskins'. The door is opened onto another room, where many guests are assembled. Anna Nikolavna and Princess Sophia enter.*]

SOPHIA: Aunt Anna! Natasha and I have just come from the shops. We bought all the things she needs. I don't know whether you will like them, but I think they are very good. The white lace is expensive, though.

ANNA NIKOLAVNA: I don't have time to look at them right now, Sonyushka. Later I will.

(*Some guests come in.*)

How do you do, Sergey Sergeich! How are you? I wasn't expecting you at all. You're so uppish: you never come to see us . . .

FIRST GUEST: Come, now! I heard that your Natasha was engaged, and I came to offer congratulations and wish her every happiness.

ANNA NIKOLAVNA: Thank you most kindly, and God grant it! The young man seems very decent.

FIRST GUEST: And he has a good fortune, so I've heard.

ANNA NIKOLAVNA: Of course! But then I suppose you know Monsieur Belinskoy?

FIRST GUEST: I have seen him off and on. He is a very fine young man.

ANNA NIKOLAVNA: Won't you please come into the drawing room, Sergey Sergeich?

(*They both go into the drawing room.*)

SOPHIA: Everything is going just the way I want it! Then why do I feel uneasy? Could it be that I have two hearts, so that one and the same thing can cause me both joy and sorrow? How can I reconcile my inner peace with the fact that what I wanted to happen, has happened. And yet, my main purpose is still far from achieved. I want to see how all this will affect Vladimir. Oh God, how I hate being in this crowd of people who talk so excitedly about trifles, never noticing how each minute takes away some of my hope and brings me a new kind of torment! Where are the unhappy ones? I see only smiles on all of their faces. I alone am weeping; I alone am drying my tears . . . If he knew, he would begin to love me. He would not be able to resist. It's impossible—impossible that he should be completely indifferent!

NATASHA (*dashing in; happy*): Ha, ha, ha! *Ma cousine,* listen to this. If you had been there, you would have died laughing. Ha, ha, ha! Oh, Lord! I held myself in until I almost laughed in his face.

SOPHIA: Whose face?

NATASHA: I broke away from him by force. Sergey Sergeich came up to wish me happiness. He got all confused, and began to stammer and mumble . . . I didn't understand a word. And I guess he himself didn't know what he was saying. It was so funny! And so we stood there looking at each other . . . Ha, ha, ha!

SOPHIA: My, but you're in a gay mood! Where is Belinskoy?

BELINSKOY (*coming in*): Thank God, here we are together again! They had me besieged for ages, like the fortress of Ochakov! They are good people, but terribly boring. They all keep talking about the past; but I'm so happy in the present!

SOPHIA: One can see it in your face.

NATASHA: Let's leave her to herself, *cher ami.* She's out of sorts. Sit down, and let's talk. (*They sit down.*)

BELINSKOY (*kissing her hand*): Now I have the right to challenge all those who envy me!

SOPHIA (*to herself*): He thinks and talks about happiness, while stealing it from his friend. Why is it that I, although less guilty, still feel remorse? Oh, how I could make up this loss to Vladimir, if only. . . .

(*A Guest, a young man, comes in from the drawing room. He bows to Sophia and comes up to her.*)

GUEST: Is your mother well, Princess?

SOPHIA: No. She is very ill.

GUEST: You know Vladimir Arbenin, do you not?

SOPHIA: He comes to our house.

GUEST: Have you noticed whether he is insane?

SOPHIA: I have always observed that he was very intelligent. I cannot imagine the point of such a question.

GUEST: I am not joking. A few days ago I was at his father's house. Suddenly the door opened noisily, and Vladimir ran into the room. I was frightened. His face was pale, his eyes were glazed, and his hair was disheveled. He looked like I don't know what. His father was petrified, and couldn't say a word. "Murderer!" Vladimir cried out. "You didn't believe me! Now go and kiss her dead hand!" And then he fell down senseless. The servants ran in and carried him off. His father didn't say a word. But he was shaking—although he acted, or tried to act, as if he were not upset . . . I quickly took my hat and left. Later I heard that Pavel Grigorich had abused him fearfully, and even cursed him. That's what they say, but I don't believe it . . .

SOPHIA (*very much disturbed*): He cursed him, you say? Vladimir fell, but wasn't hurt? You don't know what his words meant? No, that's not madness. Something terrible has happened to him.

GUEST (*smiling*): I didn't expect you would be so much concerned.

SOPHIA: Really? (*Aside, angrily.*) God! One can't even show pity!

GUEST: Finally, I learned that Vladimir's mother, who had been divorced from his father, had died that same day. But that kind of wild behavior, and those threats, are a sign of complete madness! Actually, it's a pity. He had talent, intelligence, learning . . .

SOPHIA: According to the words you have repeated to me, his father was guilty of something . . . Vladimir didn't notice you. If that's all it takes to make a person insane—

GUEST: Oh, by no means! I didn't want to tell you, but you must judge for yourself. I felt sorry for him. That's why I asked.

SOPHIA: You see that I cannot give you an affirmative answer.

GUEST (*after a pause*): Princess, are you going to the concert tomorrow night? A wonderful musician is going to play on the harp. Have you heard her? She is from Paris . . . It will be very curious. If you'd like, I can—

SOPHIA: I am not curious. I don't have that vice.

GUEST: Pardon me. I merely wanted to be of service.

SOPHIA: You are very kind.

GUEST (*bowing*): I beg you to believe that if I said something unpleasant to you, it was by no means my intention.

(*He leaves.*)

SOPHIA (*alone*): He almost said that he wanted to make me glad with such news! He came here on purpose, and stood here fifteen minutes, so that he could speak evil about one person and bring sorrow to another. (*Pause*) What awaits me? The future is growing frightfully dark before me, like an abyss eager to swallow up everything that makes life joyful for me. Vladimir has lost his mother and the love of his father. And he is going to lose Natasha too . . . But the first two blows will help him to endure the last one with firmness. A few griefs are not so dangerous as a single deep one to which all one's thoughts are chained—which poisons all feelings with the same venom. Yes, he is a man. He has a stout spirit. And there . . . there . . . I can still hope. I have noticed several times that his eyes brightened when he was talking to me. Perhaps . . .

NATASHA: What was he telling you about?

SOPHIA: About Arbenin.

BELINSKOY: What about Arbenin?

SOPHIA: You needn't be afraid.

BELINSKOY: Why should I be afraid?

SOPHIA: You know better than I do.

NATASHA (*quietly*): Do you suppose he heard that I was to be married?

SOPHIA: To his friend? No. He has lost his mother, and it has made him frantic. Some people thought he had gone insane . . . I don't know whether he'll be able to bear this new blow.

BELINSKOY: Oh, he seems much more sensitive than he really is, believe me!

SOPHIA: Naturally, you must know more about that than we do. You were his friend.

BELINSKOY: I have sacrificed friendship to love.

SOPHIA: That's very fine—for you.

BELINSKOY: Besides, you mustn't think that Vladimir

and I were really such very good friends. In this day and age, friends are like two strings on an instrument: a musician can produce harmonious sounds from them at will; but they contain an equal number of possible dissonances.

SOPHIA (*to Natasha*): Please don't be angry with me, cousin, when I say that you were in love with him. You should keep no secrets from your betrothed. Monsieur Belinskoy no doubt agrees with this.

NATASHA (*flushes at hearing these words*): Yes, that's true. I liked Arbenin at first, and he meant a good deal to me. But that dream, like all melancholy dreams, has passed away. And I must now ask you, Sophia, not to remind me of it again.

SOPHIA: For some reason I am not entirely convinced of your awakening.

BELINSKOY: Perhaps one dream has been succeeded by another.

SOPHIA: In any case, *Monsieur le fiancé,* I wouldn't put too much faith in her words. For a long time now she has been wearing in a locket some of the verses that Arbenin gave her. Tell her, please, to show them to you. Ah! Did I hit the mark, my sweet?

BELINSKOY: I can ask even that, if she is willing. Anyway, I trust her too much—

SOPHIA: Excesses are always dangerous!

NATASHA: Just to show my cousin that I care nothing for such foolish things . . . (*She takes off her necklace. From a locket in the form of a cross, she removes a slip of paper*). Take it. I had long ago forgotten that faded slip of paper. Read it, *mon ami*. The verses are rather well written.

BELINSKOY: It's his handwriting!

SOPHIA (*aside*): How brazen! He is so casual, you'd think he was reading a show bill. Not a single spark of remorse in his icy eyes! Can he be feigning? I may be a woman, but I could never be so hypocritical! Oh, why was my pure soul stained with that one spot?

NATASHA: Read it, *mon ami*.

BELINSKOY (*reading*):

When your friend has left behind him
nothing but memories
of days of madness, days of passion,
rather than a glorious name;
when others, mocking venomously,
pass judgment on the life he lived,
will you be a shield for him
against the heartless crowd?

He lived with others as with strangers;
their enmity was justified;
but although guilty in their eyes,
he was at all times true to you.
With just one tear, with just one answer,
you can wipe out the sentence passed.
Trust me! The shame for which you shed your tears
is not shameful before the world!

Beautiful! Very nice. (*He returns the slip of paper.*)

NATASHA (*tearing up the paper*): And now, cousin, will you stop worrying?

SOPHIA: Oh, I've never worried on your account!

BELINSKOY (aside): That woman rubs me the wrong way! What is the point of her reproaches? What business is it of hers?

(The door opens, and Vladimir comes in. He bows. Everyone is embarrassed. He starts to leave but, with a look at Belinskoy and Natasha, he hesitates; then he goes quickly into the drawing room.)

NATASHA (as soon as Vladimir has left): Oh! Arbenin!

BELINSKOY (to himself): How untimely! Did the devil send him? He'll go out of his mind with rage. He probably doesn't know yet that I am to be married—or who the bride is. I'd better run along so as not to be the victim of the first outburst. (Aloud) I'd rather not meet Arbenin right now. You know him . . .

SOPHIA (giving him a sidewise glance): That's right.

BELINSKOY: Well, then, proshchayte. (He goes into the study.)

NATASHA (to herself): I'm shaking all over, and my heart is pounding. . . . Why? Why does that man, whom I no longer love, still have such an effect on me? Could it be that my love for him never really died out completely? Perhaps it was only my imagination that made me drift away from him for a while. But in any case, I want to, and must, be cool toward him. I promised Belinskoy I would marry him, and I must get rid of Arbenin. That shouldn't be too difficult. (She grows thoughtful.)

SOPHIA: Thank God! (To herself) I thought Belinskoy was untroubled by his conscience, but now I see just the opposite. He was afraid to look into the eyes of the person he had deceived. So he is more guilty than I am! I saw the consternation in his face. Let him run away! But can he run away from the inevitable punishment of Heaven? (*She moves downstage.*)

Vladimir comes in from the drawing room. He is pallid. For some time, he and Natasha stand immobile.)

NATASHA: Well, what do you have to tell me that's new?

VLADIMIR: They say you're getting married.

NATASHA: That's not new to me.

VLADIMIR: I wish you every happiness.

NATASHA: Thank you very much.

VLADIMIR: Then it is really true?

NATASHA: What's so surprising about it?

VLADIMIR (*after a pause*): You won't be happy.

NATASHA: Why not?

VLADIMIR: I have heard that a marriage which takes place on the same day as a funeral is never a happy one.

NATASHA: Your predictions are very gloomy. Anyway, someone dies every day. And so—

VLADIMIR: Tell me truly: Is this a joke, or not?

NATASHA: No.

VLADIMIR: You'd better think hard about it. I swear to God that I am in no state to hear such jokes. You are capable of pity. Listen to me. I have lost my mother, an angel. My father has disowned me. I have lost everything except one spark of hope. One word from you, and that spark will go out! That's the kind of power you now possess. I came here to have a few moments of peace and happiness. What do you gain by depriving me of those moments with a joke?

NATASHA: I had no intention of joking. I quite understand that you are deeply unhappy. And I would deserve only contempt if I could joke with you now. No, you are entitled to respect and sympathy from everyone.

VLADIMIR (*after studying her for a time*): Do you remember how, a long, long time ago, I brought you a poem in which I begged your protection against the slanders of the world? And you promised me! Since then I have believed in you as in God. Since then I have loved you more than God. Oh! The tone of your voice, when you said, "I promise." And I swore to myself, then, that I would love you forever. Forever! From someone else, those words would mean very little . . . But I *swore* to love you eternally—I swore it to myself. And the oath of a noble person is as unchangeable as the will of the Creator. Answer me. Speak just one word that is not altogether cold . . . Even tell me a lie, and I will be content. What does one word cost? It will save a man from despair.

NATASHA (*aside*): What can I do? I can't think clearly. Oh, why, why can't I erase just a few days from my life, and have things as they were before? Then I could answer him. He is so miserable. I don't love him; but I am somehow frightened at the idea of hurting him.

VLADIMIR: Woman, why do you hesitate? Listen! Supposing a starving dog crawled to your feet with a pathetic whine and movements expressing the worst kind of suffering. If you had a crust of bread, would you not give it to him, when you saw the signs of starvation in his cavernous eyes—even though you had intended a very different use for that piece of bread? In the same way, I beg of you just one word of love!

NATASHA (*meaningfully, after a pause*): I am to be married to Belinskoy.

(*Sophia, who has been watching from a distance, leaves.*)

VLADIMIR: What? To Belinskoy? To him? Then my suspicions—

NATASHA: What were you afraid of?

VLADIMIR: And I called him my friend! Hell and damnation! He will pay for this! He will pay with his blood for every tear that I shed on that traitorous breast! (*He starts to leave.*)

NATASHA: Wait! Wait! (*He stands quite still.*) What madness! So this is the kind of affection you have for me! I love Belinskoy, and you want to kill him! Come to your senses! His death would compel me to hate you.

VLADIMIR: You feel sorry for him? You love him? I don't believe it. I just don't believe it. A man who has betrayed his friend is not worthy of respect. Love and contempt are incompatible. My hand will rid you of that snake!

NATASHA: Vladimir! Wait, I beg of you!

VLADIMIR (*looking at her; sighs tiredly*): All right. What else do you want me to do?

NATASHA: We must not see each other again. Forget me, I implore you. It will spare both of us a great deal of unpleasantness. For a young man, there is no lack of distractions. You will fall in love with another woman; you will marry. Then we can see each other again. We shall be friends. We can spend whole, wonderful days together. But until then, I beg of you to forget a girl who must not listen to your complaints.

VLADIMIR: Fine advice! (*He paces back and forth. Then, with a dry laugh*) From what novel did you learn these wise exhortations? What heroine are you imitating? Did you think I was some kind of Werther? A beautiful thought! Who could have expected it?

NATASHA: Your reasons tells you the same thing I am telling you. But you don't want to listen.

VLADIMIR (*aside*): No, I will not take vengeance on Belinskoy. I made a mistake. I remember: he often used to talk to me about reason. They are made for each other . . . And what does it matter to me? Let them live and get children. Let them mortgage estates and buy others . . . That's what they are suited for. Oh! To think that I would have given up years of bliss for one moment of her happiness! And what would it mean to her? What childish stupidity!

NATASHA: My words are disagreeable to you. But the truth, they say, is not pleasant to anyone. I must admit that you, your character, and your intelligence made a rather strong impression on me at first. But things have changed, now, and we must part. I love another. And so I will set an example for you: I will forget you.

VLADIMIR: You will forget me? *You?* Never believe it! Conscience is more infallible than memory. Am I likely to believe that you could forget the one who would have thrown the whole world down at your feet, if he had had to choose between you and the world? Belinskoy is not worthy of you. He will never be able to value your love, your mind. He has sacrificed a friend for . . . Oh, not for you! For money! Money! That's what he worships! And he will sacrifice you to it. Then you will curse your own inconsistency . . . Yes, and the day you gave me hopes . . . fatal hopes . . . and created an earthly paradise for my heart, so as to deprive me of a heavenly one.

NATASHA: I must tell you once more to stop this. You are speaking too freely. (*Pause*) We must not see each other any more. Why should you want to disturb a family's tranquility? This momentary outburst will pass. Then, later, we can be friends.

VLADIMIR: Aren't you counting a bit too much on your own virtue? No, I cannot live on the leftovers from a treasure belonging to another! What is it you dare to propose to me? Good God! Now I can see that the evil spirits were formerly angels!

NATASHA: Monsieur Arbenin, I find your obstinacy and impudence quite impossible to bear. You are insufferable!

VLADIMIR: Why didn't you talk like this to me before?

NATASHA: You are right. I was ridiculous . . . stupid. How can one expect a madman to behave like a reasonable person? I must leave you now. I admit that I am sorry that I tried to console someone. You have completely disregarded all the decencies of behavior, and I do not intend to put up with anything more! (*She walks away; but stops, downstage, and watches him.*)

VLADIMIR: Oh God! At this moment I have neither love for You nor belief in You. But do not punish me for my rebellious mutterings. You Yourself, through my unbearable torments, have provoked these blasphemies. Why did You give me a passionate heart that can love beyond all measure, but cannot hate in the same way? You are guilty! Let Your thunderbolt strike my unbowed head! I cannot think that the last outcry of a perishing insect gives You joy!

(*During this speech, Belinskoy has entered. Natasha*

whispers something in his ear, evidently asking a favor of him, and then leaves. He watches Vladimir from a distance, as the latter wrings his hands.)

Those tender lips, that enchanting voice, her smile, her eyes—all that has become a hell for me! How could she have given me those hopes, merely to have the satisfaction of blighting them once more! (*He wipes his eyes and forehead.*) Oh, woman! Are you worth these bloody tears?

(*Belinskoy comes up to him.*)

BELINSKOY: Vladimir! (*Aside*) I'll have to coax him and be persuasive. Otherwise he'll commit God knows what kind of folly! Natasha is right. It's only during the first moments of madness that he's dangerous. (*Aloud*) Vladimir!

VLADIMIR (*without turning around*): What?

BELINSKOY: Are you angry with me?

VLADIMIR: No.

BELINSKOY: Oh, I can see that you're angry. But she herself made the choice, didn't she?

VLADIMIR (*still without turning around*): Of course.

BELINSKOY: Time will heal you.

VLADIMIR: I don't know about that. (*His voice shakes.*)

BELINSKOY: Arbenin! It's plain to see that you are terribly angry with me. Believe me: I know you very well. I have come to know all the movements of your heart. Sometimes I can explain your behavior better than my own.

VLADIMIR: You know me? You can say that? (*He laughs.*) If that's true, then Dmitry Vasilich Belinskoy is either the greatest fool or the greatest villain in the world!

BELINSKOY: I'd rather be the former than the latter.

VLADIMIR: I congratulate you.

BELINSKOY: But judge for yourself. Didn't I have the same right to her hand as you did? You, my friend, are an egotist. Believe me: your grief is nothing more than wounded pride.

VLADIMIR: You mean I should believe you?

BELINSKOY: Do you really think I abused your trust? Did I reveal any of your secrets? Natasha loved you first, I admit. But now it's my turn. Why didn't you marry her then?

VLADIMIR: I advise you to leave me. Don't count too much on my self-possession. I was all ready to take vengeance on you—to have your blood. Your blood, do you hear? But I forgive you and accuse you of nothing. Only you must leave me. I cannot make reply to your sincere blandishments. (*He laughs wildly.*) Now I am free. Nobody—absolutely nobody on this earth—cares about me. Do you hear? And *you* did it! Don't be afraid . . . And don't have any regrets. What does it matter? I am superfluous! You are a clever, cautious, and intelligent man. You saw that friendship was softening me—that hope was coddling me—and at one stroke you took away everything! Belinskoy! It would seem that now I have nothing to be envied!

BELINSKOY: You have not forgiven me. That coldness—that venomous smile!

VLADIMIR: Oh, you have judged too well of me. For some time, now, I have had no more obligations toward you, monetary or other . . .

BELINSKOY: And so you have no more affection for me at all? Do you mean we shall never again see each other, even if I prove—

VLADIMIR: For what purpose?

BELINSKOY: I adjure you.

VLADIMIR (*aside*): What baseness! To think that she can love him, and that I once did myself!

BELINSKOY: In her name, I beg of you.

VLADIMIR: Enough, enough! Do you think there is anything else to be taken away from me?

BELINSKOY (*through clenched teeth*): He's absolutely unbending! (*To Vladimir*) Listen. You must forgive me. It's too late to change anything now. But in the future, I give you my word of honor—

VLADIMIR: Enough, I tell you!

BELINSKOY: Just think about it. In time—

VLADIMIR (*aside*): In time, in time! Almighty God! Why did you allow her to sacrifice my love to such a contemptible person?

BELINSKOY: You don't even want to listen to an experienced friend who wishes you well.

VLADIMIR (*to himself*): Merciful God!

BELINSKOY: So that's the way it is. I must not leave you— it is my duty not to. And later on, you yourself will be grateful. It would be a crime not to hold back a madman on the brink of the precipice. (*He takes him by the arm.*) Let's go to her! Natasha will soothe your grief. You told me that one look from her could calm your inner turmoil . . . Let's go to her.

(*He tries to lead him away; but Vladimir remains im-*

mobile for a moment, then breaks from his grasp and runs out.)

Stop! Stop! *(Pause)* He has gone! I have fulfilled the wish of my fiancée, and fate will fulfill mine. But why couldn't I breathe freely in his presence? After all, I am in the right—everybody agrees on that. Is Arbenin a child who throws himself into the river because he fears the rod? What stupid jealousy! He hates me because she prefers me to him. It's too bad that such a good mind should be victimized by a senseless passion. Why is it he can't control himself?

(Princess Sophia comes in.)

SOPHIA: Where is Arbenin?

BELINSKOY: He has left. He was like somebody in a trance. He ran out of the door like a madman.

SOPHIA: And you didn't hold him back? Does he still love Natasha?

BELINSKOY: More than ever.

SOPHIA *(She grows pale, and falls into an armchair)*: So it was all in vain!

BELINSKOY: What's the matter? Boy! Bring her some spirits and water!

SOPHIA: Leave me alone!

Scene XIII

EPILOGUE

[*May 12, evening. The home of Count N——— Many guests. Tea is being served.*]

FIRST GUEST: Did you hear the news, Count? Tomorrow there will be a wedding at our parish church. Would you like to go?

COUNT: A wedding? Whose?

FIRST GUEST: The Zagorskina girl is marrying Belinskoy.

FIRST LADY: Do you know the bridegroom?

SECOND GUEST: I know him.

FIRST LADY: Is he rich?

SECOND GUEST: He has an estate, and therefore he has debts.

FIRST LADY: Is he handsome?

SECOND GUEST: Very. But he pays too much attention to his own face.

FIRST LADY: That means he pays attention to a handsome face.

SECOND LADY: And the bride?

SECOND GUEST: Quite pretty. *Une figure piquante.*

FIRST LADY (*to her friend*): *Ma chère,* I've heard she is coquettish beyond all belief!

SECOND GUEST: She has turned the head of more than one young man.

THIRD GUEST: Yes, that poor Arbenin! You know of course that he had gone mad?

VARIOUS VOICES: Young Arbenin? No, I hadn't heard. Why did he go mad?

THIRD GUEST: Why? Out of love for the Zagorskina girl. I heard he was in a pathetic state. He constantly has the impression that somebody is trying to drag him off somewhere. He clings to everybody, as though for protection against a mysterious power. He laughs and cries at the same time. He will be whimpering, and then suddenly he will break out laughing. Sometimes he recognizes the people around—all but his father. He is always looking for his father. And at times he will accuse him of some murder or other.

SECOND GUEST: I'd like to know where insane people get ideas like that.

FIRST GUEST: I have heard that he was a completely worthless boy. It is surprising how respectable fathers almost always have sons like that.

FOURTH GUEST: Yes, Pavel Grigorich is a respectable man in every way.

THIRD GUEST (half in mockery): He wanted to send his son to the insane asylum, but they advised him against it. As a matter of fact, they probably blamed the whole thing on his stinginess.

SECOND LADY: And doesn't the Zagorskina girl have any qualms of conscience?

THIRD GUEST: You'll have to ask her father confessor about that.

FIRST GUEST: Is it really true that Arbenin can't be cured? Perhaps there is some physical cause. Strange! Imagine going mad because of love.

THIRD GUEST: If that seems strange to you, I would like to see one of these ladies here try to show you that it isn't!

FIRST GUEST: But I'm talking about Arbenin. In social gatherings he always seemed to be gay and carefree, as though his heart were a soap bubble.

THIRD GUEST: You are not, of course, a student of Lavater? Besides, even if he did seem gay-spirited at times, that was only a mask. As one can see from his private papers and his behavior, he had an impetuous nature and a restless soul. Some deep-lying grief from early childhood was gnawing at him. God only knows what caused it. His heart matured before his mind did. He came to know the bad side of life when he was still too young to beware of its shock effects, or to endure them with indifference. There was no real gaiety in his laughter. Instead, it showed his bitter disappointment in all of humanity. True, there were moments when his naturally generous feelings would predominate. But even the slightest insult would make him furious—especially when it affected his pride. In his room they found a great many notebooks in which he had jotted down his innermost thoughts. They contain poems and prose pieces—deep thoughts and tempestuous emotions. I am convinced that if his passions had not destroyed him so early, he could have become one of our best writers. The stamp of genius can be seen in his jottings.

SECOND LADY: In my opinion, such madmen are very fortunate. They haven't a care for anything. They don't think, they don't feel sorrow, they desire nothing, and they fear nothing.

THIRD GUEST: How do you know that? The only difference with them is that they cannot remember their feelings and tell them to others. This makes their torments even worse. The soul of such a person is not deprived of its natural faculties. But the organs that express the emotions are weakened and disturbed because of excessive tension. Constant chaos reigns in his head. Only one half-perceived thought remains fixed, while other thoughts revolve around it in complete disorder. This results from a sudden shock to all of the nerves—to the entire physical system—which is no doubt very hard on a man. Are wan cheeks and sunken, lustreless eyes indications of happiness? If you look very closely at a painting, you won't be able to distinguish anything: the colors will run together before your eyes. In the same way, a person who has looked too closely at his life is no longer able to make anything out of it. And even if something from that life remains with him, it is no more than a confused memory of the past. This state in a human being is called *madness* —and its victims are the object of laughter!

(*During this speech, many of the guests have wandered off.*)

SECOND GUEST (*to another*): I'm yawning!

FOURTH GUEST (*quietly*): Why all this speechmaking? Is he trying to make a show of his knowledge?

FIFTH GUEST (*a young man of nineteen; he comes up to the Third Guest*): Please, can you get one of Arbenin's compositions for me?

THIRD GUEST: With pleasure, if it is possible.

(*A Servant enters and hands a card to the Count, who has finished playing cards.*)

SERVANT: From Pavel Grigorich Arbenin.

(*He leaves. Everyone is astounded.*)

VARIOUS VOICES: What does this mean?

THIRD GUEST: Edged in black . . . It's an invitation to a funeral.

COUNT: Now we shall see! (*He puts on his glasses and reads aloud.*)

"Pavel Grigorevich Arbenin announces with the greatest sorrow the death of his son, Vladimir Pavlovich Arbenin, which occurred on the afternoon of May 11. You are most humbly requested to attend the funeral procession on May 13 at 10 o'clock in the evening. Services will be held at the parish church . . ." etc.

THIRD GUEST (*to himself*): Just imagine. A funeral on the same day as the Zagorskina girl's wedding!

SEVERAL GUESTS: Good Heavens! What a pity!

SECOND LADY: The poor father!

FIFTH GUEST: The poor young man! He might have been cured!

THIRD LADY (*to the Third Guest*): Pitiful, isn't it?

THIRD GUEST (*aside*): *Now* they are sorry! Toward the dead, they are just! But what does their sympathy amount to? One tear from a friend is worth all the exclamations of the crowd. But it isn't likely that such a tear will fall on Arbenin's grave. In those hearts where he wanted to instill love, he left only a gnawing conscience.

OLD LADY: No doubt the funeral will be splendid. After all, he was an only son!

THIRD GUEST (*to another Guest*): It seems to me that old ladies are fond of talking about funerals only so that they can get used to the idea: "Soon, I too will be dragged into the grave."

FIRST GUEST: Let's forget the dead. They're no concern of ours.

THIRD GUEST: If everyone thought like that, it would go hard on great men!

FIRST GUEST: I suspect your Arbenin was not a great man. He was *a strange one*, that's all.

(*The Third Guest shrugs his shoulders and walks away.*)

CURTAIN